70 YEARS OF POPULAR MUSIC

THE TWENTIES

Part Three

Production: Stephen Clark and Sadie Cook

Music processed by
Barnes Music Engraving Ltd, East Sussex TN22 4HA, UK

First published 1994
Updated edition 1996

AIN'T SHE SWEET

Cm
G7
Cm
G7♭9/C
Cm
G7♭9/C
Cm
Oh, gee whiz! Oh, gee whiz! There's why I can't eat a bite.
I de - clare, I de - clare, that sure is worth look-ing at.
L.H.
B♭7
E♭
C7
Those flam - ing eyes! That flam - ing youth!
Oh boy, how sweet those lips must be!
B♭/F
Gm
Cm
F7
B♭7
Oh, mis - ter! Oh, sis - ter! Tell me the truth.
Gaze on it! Dog - gon it! Now an - swer me!
CHORUS X 2
INTRO
E♭
Edim7
3fr
B♭7
E♭
Edim7
3fr
B♭7
Ain't she sweet? See her com - ing down the street! Now I
p-f

E♭
G7
C7
F7
B♭7
ask you ve - ry con - fi - den - tial - ly, ain't she
E♭
B♭7
E♭
Edim7
3fr
B♭7
E♭
Edim7
3fr
sweet? Ain't she nice? Look her o - ver once or
B♭7
E♭
G7
C7
F7
B♭7
twice. Now I ask you ve - ry con - fi - den - tial - ly, ain't she
E♭
E♭7
A♭7
E♭
nice? Just cast an eye in her di - rec - tion,

E♭7
A♭7
E♭
— oh me, oh my! Ain't that per - fec - tion?
B♭11
B♭7
E♭
Edim7
3fr
B♭7
E♭
Edim7
3fr
— I re - peat, don't you think that's kind of
B♭7
E♭
G7
C7
neat, and I ask you ve - ry con - fi - den - tial - ly,
F7
B♭7
1.
E♭
Edim7
3fr
B♭7
B♭aug
2.
E♭
A♭7
E♭
D.𝄋
ain't she sweet?
sweet?

AMONG MY SOUVENIRS

Words by EDGAR LESLIE
Music by HORATIO NICHOLLS

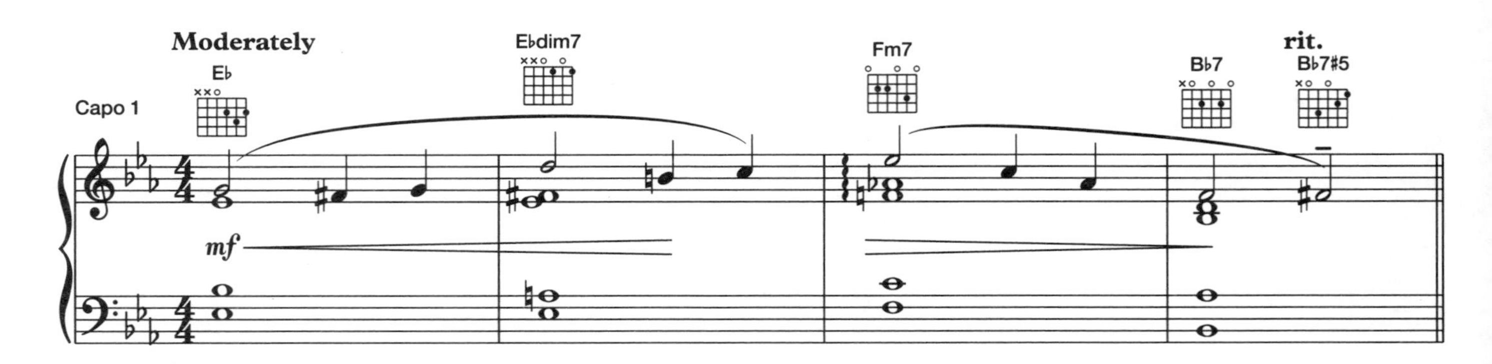

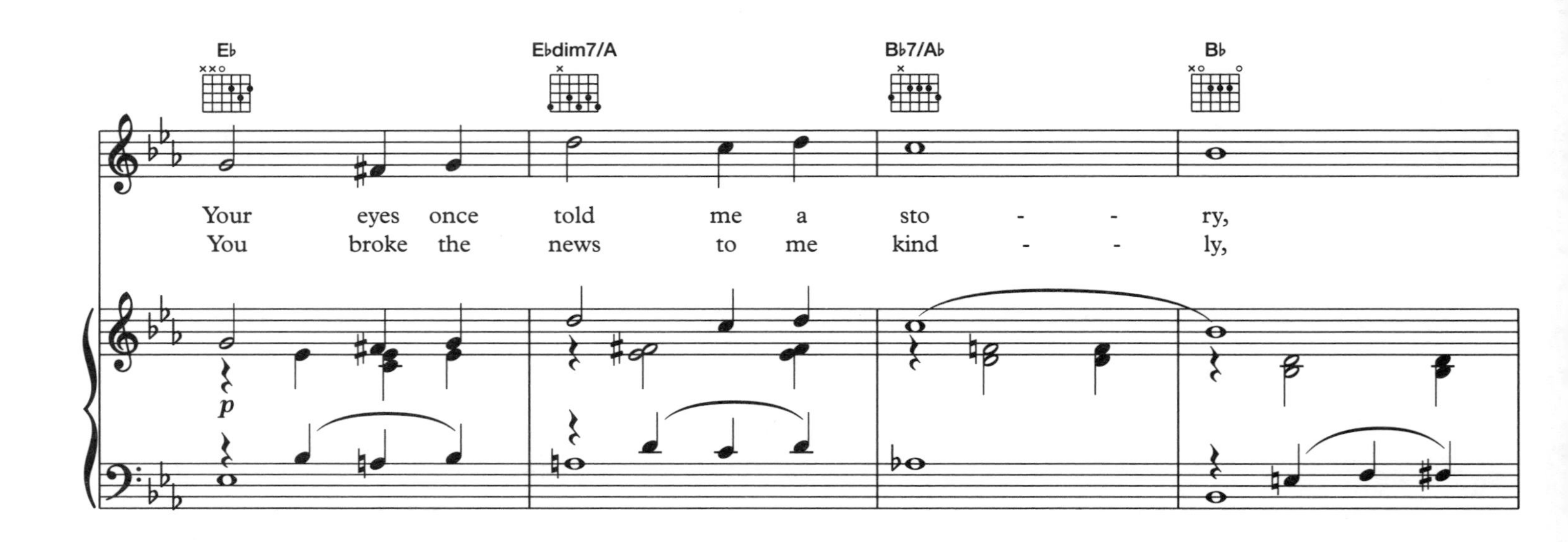

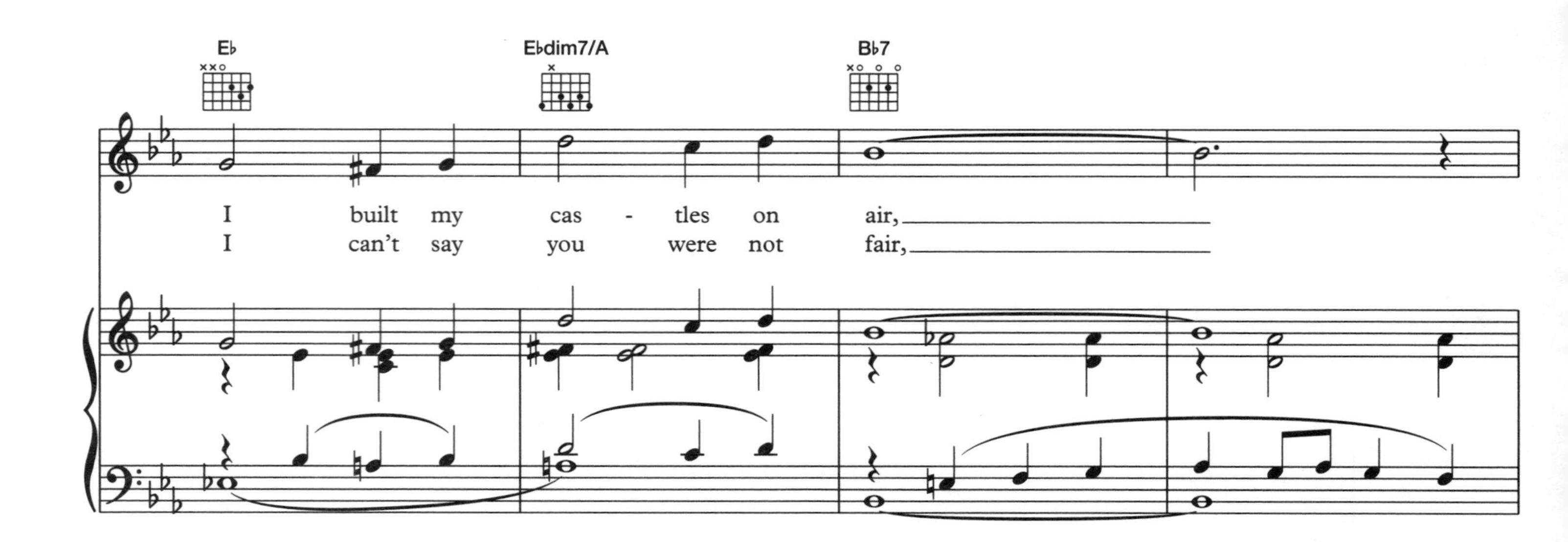

Eb7
Ab
life soon was dimmed of its glo - - ry,
yet, just be - cause I loved blind - - ly,
F7
Bb
Bbdim7
Bb7
Bb7#5
rit.
I loved, but you ceased to care.
I have the bur - den to bear.
rit.
a tempo
Eb
small notes for duet
Edim7
Bb7
Bb7#5
Eb
There's no - thing left for me, of days that used to be,
a tempo
p–f
Ebdim7/F#
Fm7
Bb
Bb7
Eb
they're just a me - mo - ry a - mong my sou - ven - irs.

Edim7
B♭7
B♭7♯5
E♭
Some letters tied with blue, a photo - graph or two,
E♭dim/F♯
Fm7
B♭
B♭7
E♭
I see a rose from you a - mong my sou - ven - irs.
E♭7
A♭
A♭m/C♭
B♭7
B♭7♯5
E♭
A few more tok - ens rest with - in my trea - sure chest,
B♭/F
Edim7
B♭7
F7
and though they do their best to bring me con - so -

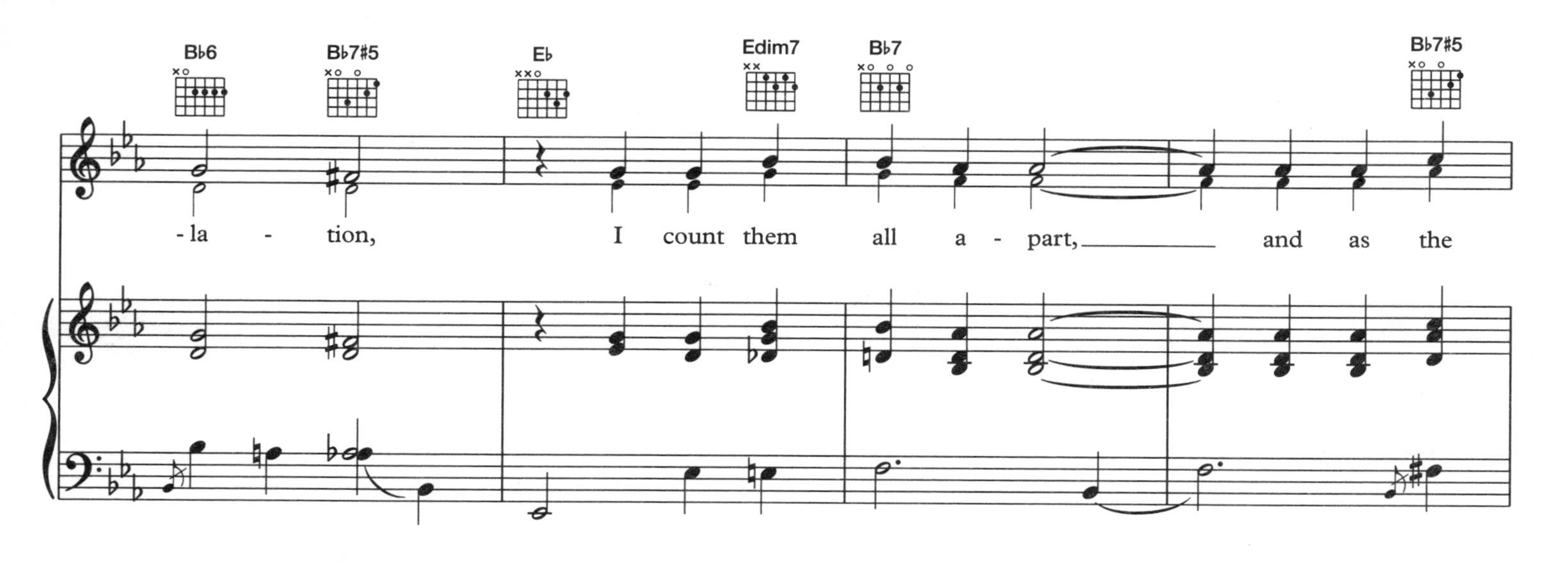
B♭6
B♭7♯5
E♭
Edim7
B♭7
B♭7♯5
-la - tion,
I count them all a - part,
and as the

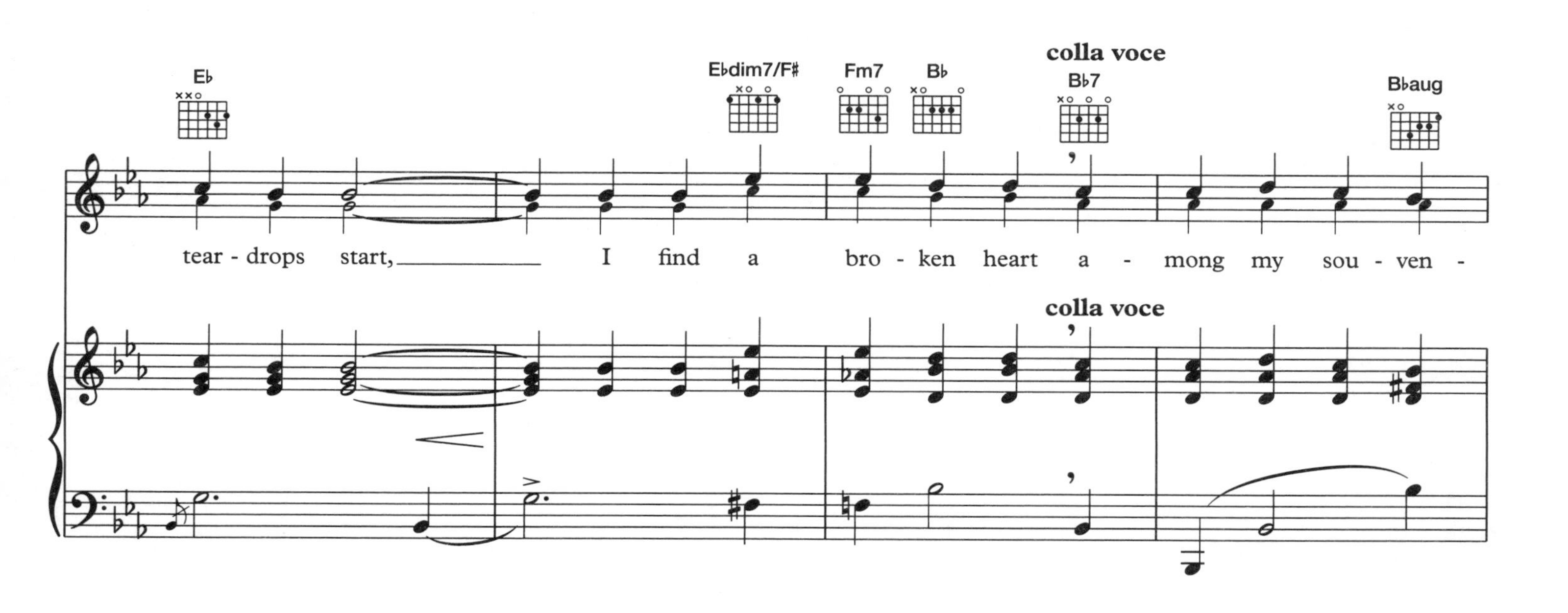
E♭
E♭dim7/F♯
Fm7
B♭
colla voce
B♭7
B♭aug
tear - drops start,
I find a bro - ken heart a - mong my sou - ven -
colla voce

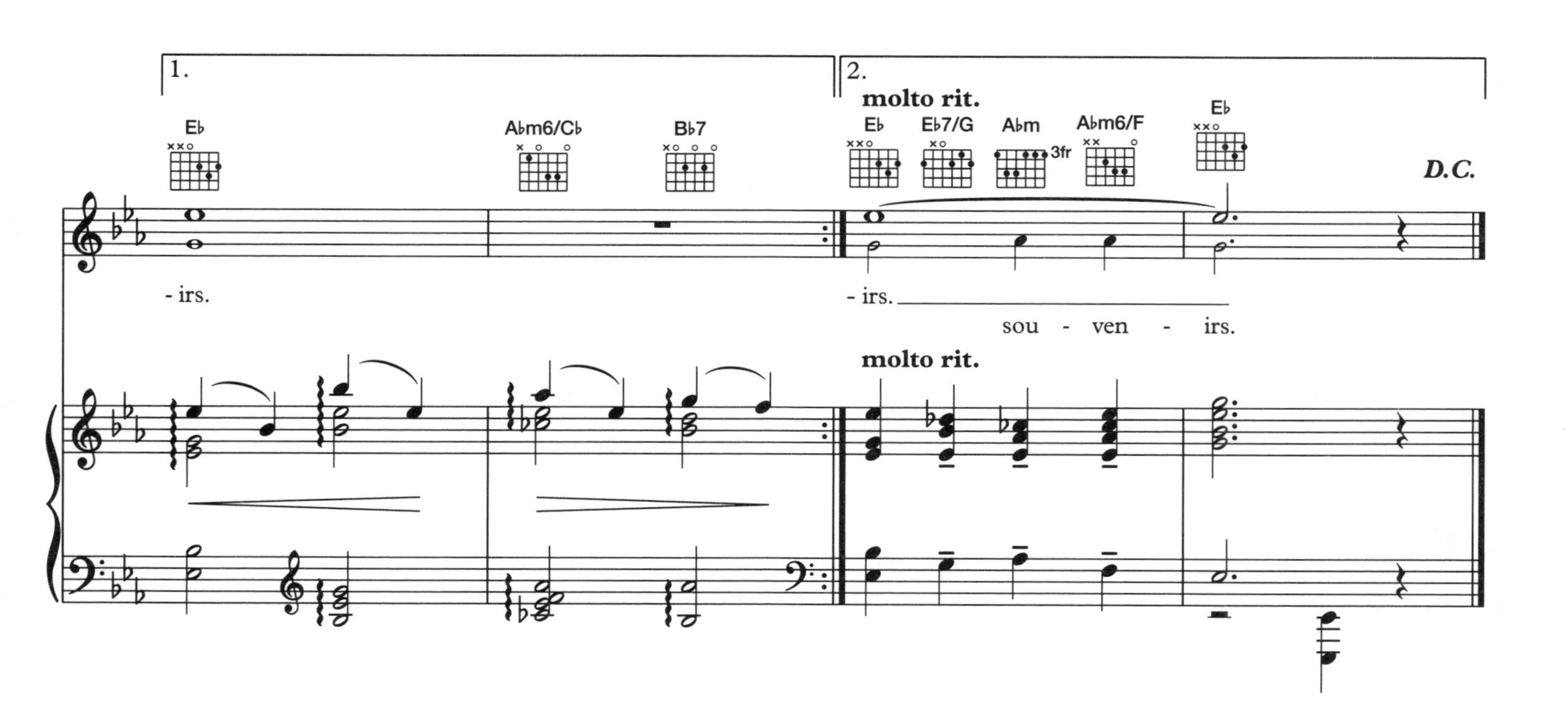
1.
2.
molto rit.
E♭
A♭m6/C♭
B♭7
E♭
E♭7/G
A♭m
3fr
A♭m6/F
E♭
D.C.
- irs.
- irs.
sou - ven - irs.
molto rit.

BABY FACE

Words and Music by BENNY DAVIS and HARRY AKST

C
G7
C
G7
now.
wise.
Pret - ty lit - tle dim - ples here and
Not a touch of paint or pow - der
C
C/E
Cm6/E♭
G/D
D7
dim - ples there,
a - ny - where,
don't want to live with -
she's sweet as moun - tain
G
Cm6/E♭
G/D
D7/F♯
G
Cm6/E♭
- out her, I love her, good - ness knows! I
dai - sies, as fresh as morn - ing dew. All
G/D
D7
G
E
E7♭9/G♯
3fr
D7
G7
wrote a song a - bout her, and here's the way it goes.
day I sing her prai - ses, and all the night - time too.

C
A♭7
4fr
C
C♯dim7
3fr
Ba - by face, you've got the cu - test lit - tle
Dm
G7
C♯dim7
3fr
G7
ba - by face, there's not an - oth - er one could
G7♭9
G7
C
Gm6/B♭
A7♭9
A7
D7
take your place, ba - by face, my poor heart
G7
C
is jump - in', you sure have start - ed some - thin'. Ba - by face,

Ab7
4fr
C
E7
I'm up in hea - ven when I'm in your
Am
C7/G
C7
F6
F#dim7
fond em - brace. I did - n't need a shove 'cause I just
C
A7
D7
G7
fell in love with your pret - ty ba - by
1.
C
Ab
4fr
2.
C
Ab
4fr
C
D.𝄋
face.
face.
fz

CAROLINA MOON

Words and Music by BENNY DAVIS and JOE BURKE

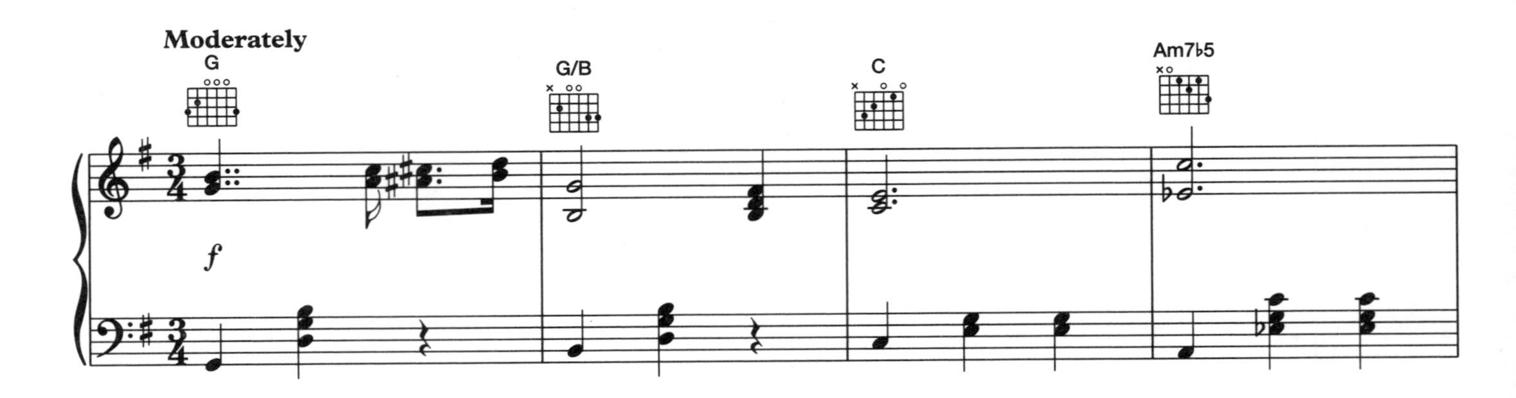

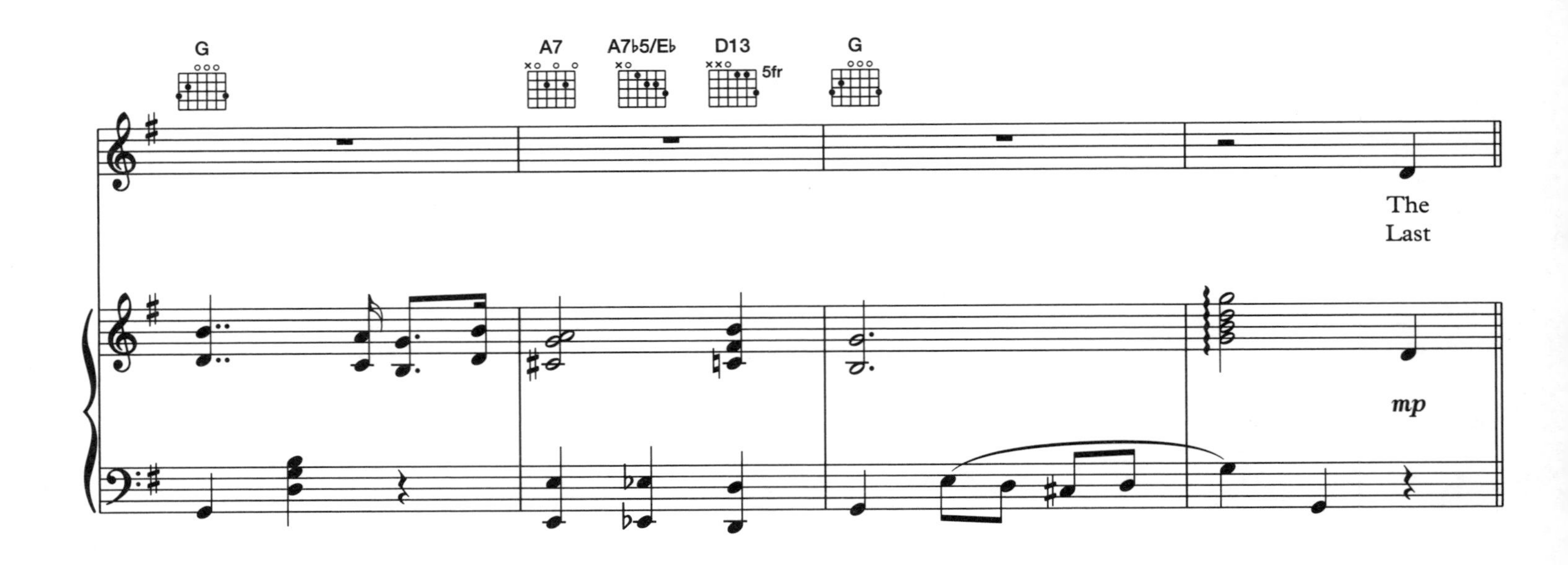

D7/F#
D7
G
G7
Gdim7
Cm6/G
G
night we said good - bye so ten - der - ly, and
dreamed that I was back there once a - gain. The
D/F#
Fdim7
now that I'm a - way from Ca - ro - li - - na,
moon was shin - ing bright in Ca - ro - li - - na,
rit.
A7/E
A7
D7
D7#5
won't some-bo - dy tell the moon for me? Oh!
shin - ing on the same old wind - ing lane. Oh!
rit.

dreamily
G
G/B
C
Am7♭5
Ca - ro - li - na moon, keep shin - - ing,
dreamily
G/D
D7
G
Gdim7
G
G/D
shin - ing on the one who waits for me.
G
G/B
C
Am7♭5
G/D
Ca - ro - li - na moon, I'm pin - - ing, pin - ing for the
D7
G
Em
G7/D
C
place I long to be. How I'm hop - ing to-night
3

G/D
G
A7
you'll go, go to the right win - dow, scat - ter your light,
D7
D7#5
G
say I'm all right, please do.
Tell her that I'm
G/B
C
Am7♭5
G/D
A7
A7♭5/E♭
D7
blue and lone - ly, drea - my Ca - ro - li - na
1.
G
D7
D7#5
2.
G
D.C.
moon.
moon.

CHICAGO (THAT TODDLING TOWN)

Words and Music by FRED FISHER

E♭
E♭dim7
Fm7/A♭
B♭9/F
E♭
Cm
be. You may not care for to be there, but I de-
Flo. A-ny ho-tel that's a bit swell must have a
mf
p
mp
E♭
Cm
F9
F11
F9/C
-clare, you're not a-ware just where to go. When you're in
band right here on hand or else they're cheap. If you'll in-
mf
mp
Fm7
B♭13
Fm7
B♭13
B♭13♭9
E♭
Edim7
Fm7
B♭13
B♭11
3fr
town, just call a-round, right there I'm found, real-ly you ought to know. Chi-
-vest, you'll find a guest, they'll ne-ver rest, they're danc-ing while they sleep.
mf

E♭maj7
E♭6
E♭maj7
E♭6
Edim7
Fm7
B♭7
Fm7
B♭9
-ca - go, Chi - ca - go, that tod-dl-ing town, Chi -
Fm7
B♭9
Fm7
B♭9
A♭dim
2fr
E♭/G
F♯dim7
Fm7
B♭9
-ca - go, Chi - ca - go, I'll show you a - round. I love it,
E♭
B♭7♯5
E♭maj7
F9
F7
F9
F7
Edim7
bet your bot - tom dol - lar you lose the blues in Chi - ca - go, Chi - ca - go, the
Fm7
B♭9
Fm7
B♭9
Gm7
C7
Fm7
B♭7
B♭11
3fr
E♭maj7
E♭
town that Bil - ly Sun-day could not shut down. On State Street, that

E♭maj7
E♭
Edim7
Fm7
B♭7
Fm7
B♭9
Fm7
B♭9
great street I just want to say,
they do things they
Dm7sus4
G7
Cm7
C7
A♭maj7
D♭9
don't do on Broad - way.
Say,
they have the time, the time of their life,
E♭6
F♯dim7
B♭7
F♯dim7
B♭7/F
B♭11
3fr
B♭7
I saw a man, he danced with his wife, in Chi - ca - go, Chi - ca - go, my home
1.
E♭
Edim7
Fm7
B♭13
B♭11
3fr
2.
E♭
B♭7♭9
E♭6/9
4fr
D.C.
town.
Chi -
town.

DANCE LITTLE LADY

Words and Music by NOEL COWARD

A♭7
A♭7♯5
D♭
C
where your path is lead-ing to, you'd be-come less wild,
D♭7
F♯7
C7
F7
but I know it's vain try - ing to ex - plain,
B♭7
E♭
A♭maj7
A♭dim
2fr
B♭
B♭13
while there's this in - sane mu - sic in your
tempo I
E♭
brain.
tempo I
f - p

allegretto grazioso

Eb Cm Ab Fm7b5 Eb/Bb

Dance, dance, dance lit-tle la-dy! Youth is fleet - ing to the rhy - thm beat-

allegretto grazioso

p

Bb7 Eb Eb6 Ebaug Eb Gm Gbaug

- ing in your mind.______ Dance, dance, dance lit-tle la-dy!

mp

Bb/F Fmaj7#5 Cm F7 F11 F7#5

So ob - sessed___ with sec - ond best, no rest____ you'll ev - er

Bb Bb7 Eb7

find.______ Time and tide and trou - ble ne - ver, ne - ver

mp

A♭6
F7
wait, let the caul - dron bub - ble, jus - ti - fy your
B♭7
E♭
F7
F♭7♯9
E♭7
fate. Dance, dance, dance lit - tle la - dy! Dance, dance, dance lit - tle la - dy!
p
Fm7
B♭7
E♭
Leave to - mor - row be - hind.
mf - p
tempo di Charleston
F7
F♯7
A♭7
B♭7
Fm
When the sax - o-phone gives a wic - ked moan, Charle - ston, hey! Hey!
tempo di Charleston
mf

Fm7
Adim7
Gm
Rhy - thms_ fall and_ rise, start danc - ing
C7
to the tune_ the band's croon-ing, for soon the night_ will be gone. Start sway - ing
Fm
Fm6
Fm6
B♭7
like a reed_ with-out heed - ing the speed that hur - ries you on.
p
B♭13sus4
B♭13
F7
F♯7
A♭7
B♭7
Nig - ger me - lo-dies syn - co - pate_ your nerves till your bo - dy curves,

E♭7
E♭aug
droop - ing,
stoop - ing,
laugh - ter
some day
A♭6
E♭/B♭
Gm
A♭
Fm7♭5
dies,
and when the lights are start - ing to gut - ter,
E♭/G
Caug
C7
F7
F♯7
A♭7
dawn through the shut - ter
shows you're liv - ing in a
B♭7
E♭
world of lies.
mf - p

allegretto
Eb Cm Ab Fm7b5 Eb/Bb
Dance, dance, dance lit-tle la-dy! Youth is fleet - ing to the rhy - thm beat-
allegretto
p
Bb7 Eb Eb6 Ebaug Eb Gm Gbaug
- ing in your mind. Dance, dance, dance lit-tle la-dy!
mp
Bb/F Fmaj7#5 Cm F7 F11 F7#5 Bb
So ob sessed with sec-ond best, no rest you'll ev - er find.
Bb7 Eb7
Time and tide and trou-ble ne - ver, ne - ver wait,
mp

Ab6
F7
Bb7
Eb
let the caul - dron bub - ble, jus - ti - fy your fate. Dance, dance,
p
F7
Fb7#9
Eb7
Fm7
Bb7
dance lit - tle la - dy! Dance, dance, dance lit - tle la - dy! Leave your trou - bles be -
1.
2. andante, quasi pesante
A7
- hind.
- hind.
andante, quasi pesante
mf - p
f
B7
Eb6
fz

DEEP IN MY HEART, DEAR

Words by DOROTHY DONNELLY
Music by SIGMUND ROMBERG

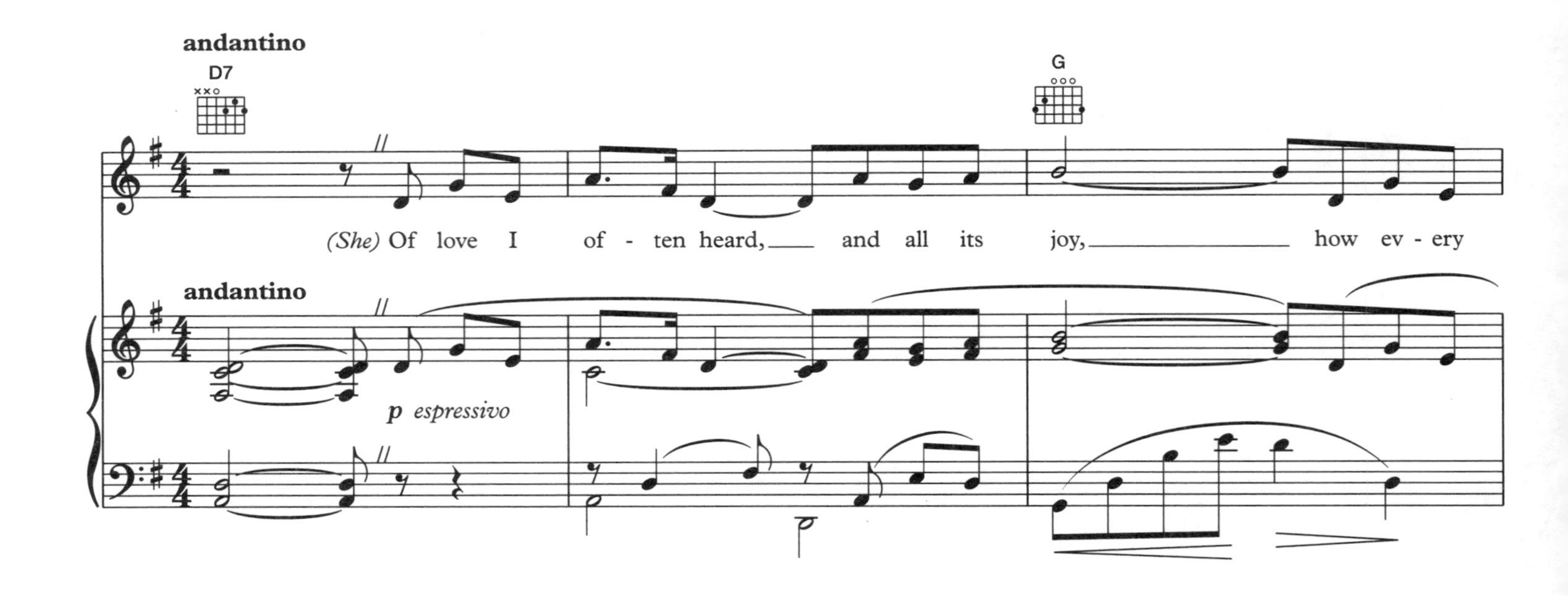

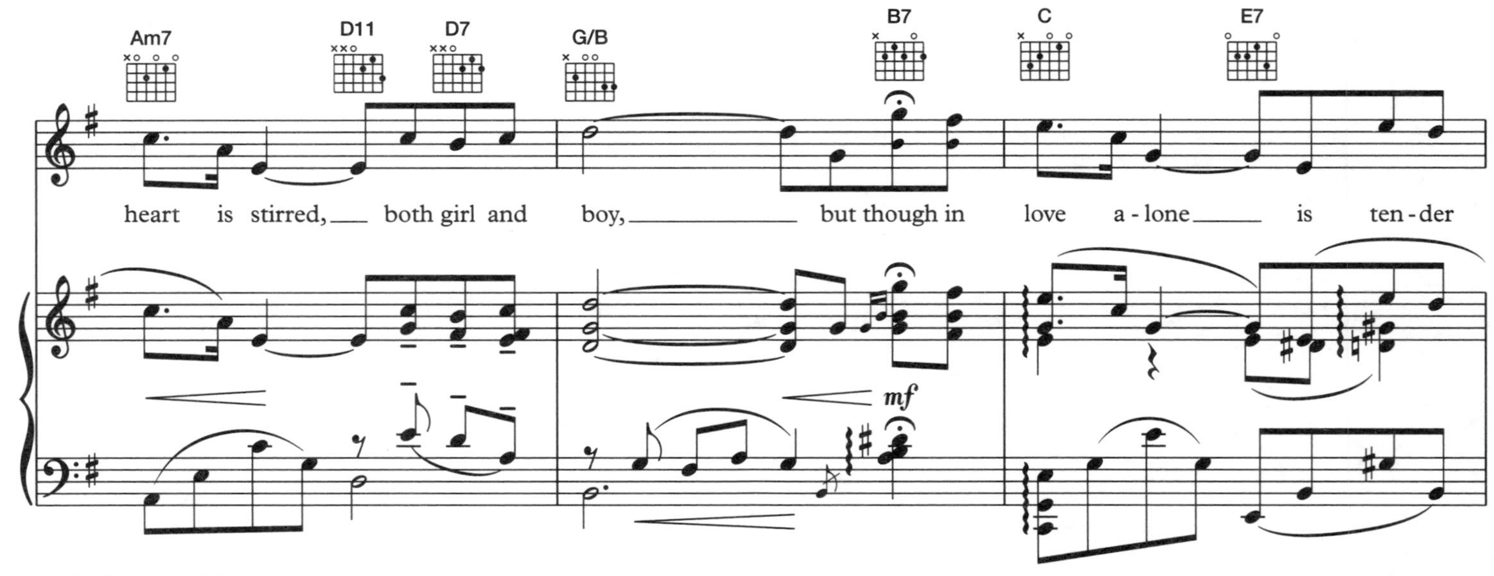

Am
A7♭9/E♭
G/D
D7
G
bliss, my lips have ne - ver known a lov - er's kiss.
(He) Oh,
valse moderato
Dmaj7
tell me if with - in your heart, you know a ten - der
valse moderato
A7/E
B♯dim7
A7
Aaug
long - ing sweet as mine, a
più espress.
Em
Em7/D
F♯m/C♯
A
spell that fills me full of joy, and though my veins like
più espress.

D/F#
A
D
più mosso
Em
wine runs joy di - vine.
più mosso
mf
A13
D/F#
sempre accell.
D6/A
A11
3fr
C#7
D/F#
It is the spring that's call - ing you and
sempre accell.
cresc.
rit.
F#aug
meno mosso
G
G#dim7
D/A
D/F#
me. Joy is in the air! Cast a - way all care!
rit.
meno mosso
f allarg.
Em7
A7
Dmaj7
più mosso
Em
Ev - ery song that's sung tells us we are young! (Hums) Hm,
più mosso
cresc.

A13 D/A D6/A A11 3fr C#7 D/F#
(She) Is this some spell of ma - gic
hm, hm, hm,
molto cresc.
rit. F#aug molto allarg. G G#dim7 D/A molto rit. E7/B
May? Ma - gic of the May! Oh, her call we must o -
Ma - gic of the May! Oh, her call we must o -
molto allarg. rit. 8va molto rit.
f
D/A slowly Em A7 allegretto D
- bey, and fol - low her flower - strewn way!
- bey, and fol - low her flower - strewn way!
slowly allegretto
ff pp

Gm/D
A7♭9/D
D
Gm
C#dim7
C7
rit.
(He) The
p
valse (molto espress.)
F
F#dim7
ma - gic of spring-time is round us to - night. En - chant-ment is borne on the
mf
C7
Gm
breeze, (She) and clothed in the sil - ver of ten - der moon - light, the
C11
C7
Caug
F
birds mur - mur soft in the trees. (He) As deep in the sha - dow your

rall.
A7/E
E9
A
eyes look in mine, with - in them a soft flame gent - ly glows.
(Both) The
mf
L.H.
f
allarg.
a tempo
B♭dim7
B♭
B♭dim7
B♭
F/C
F/A
Gm
3fr
C7
breath of the night-wind with per - fume di - vine is filled with the scent of the
8va
mf
F
B♭dim7
B♭
B♭dim7
B♭
F/C
D7
rose. Oh love, while I live I will al - ways en - shrine your
(She)
p

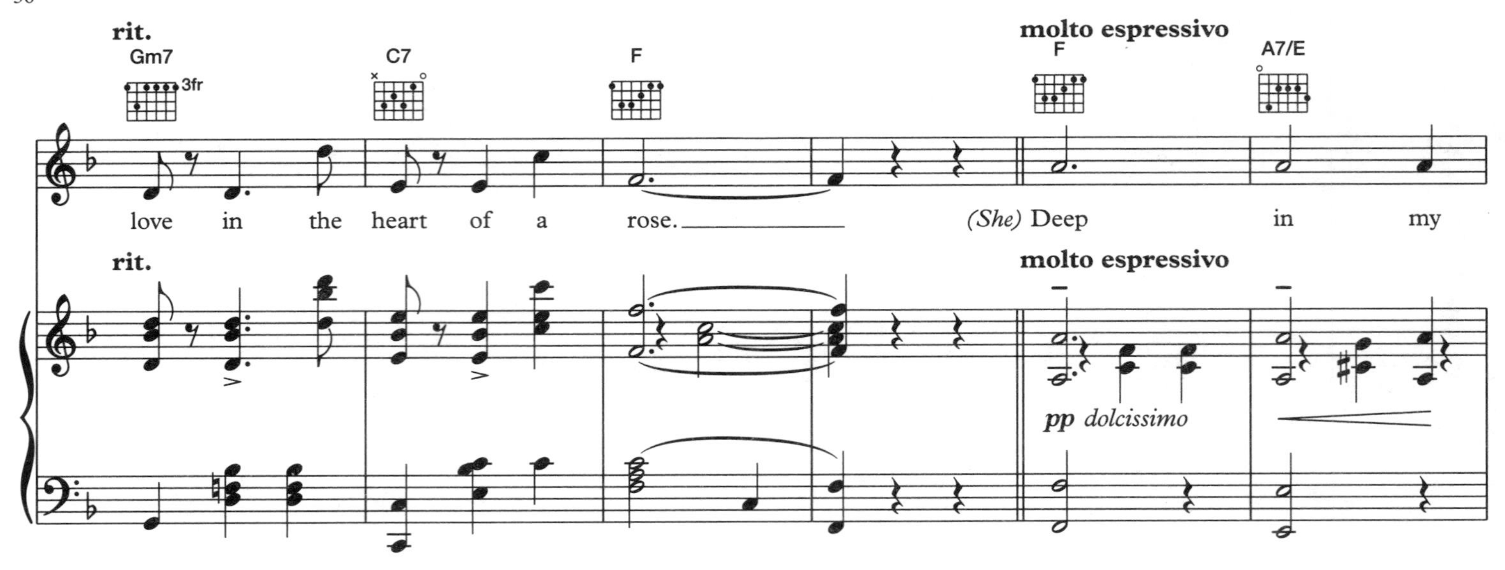
rit.
Gm7
3fr
C7
F
molto espressivo
F
A7/E
love in the heart of a rose.
(She) Deep in my
rit.
molto espressivo
pp dolcissimo

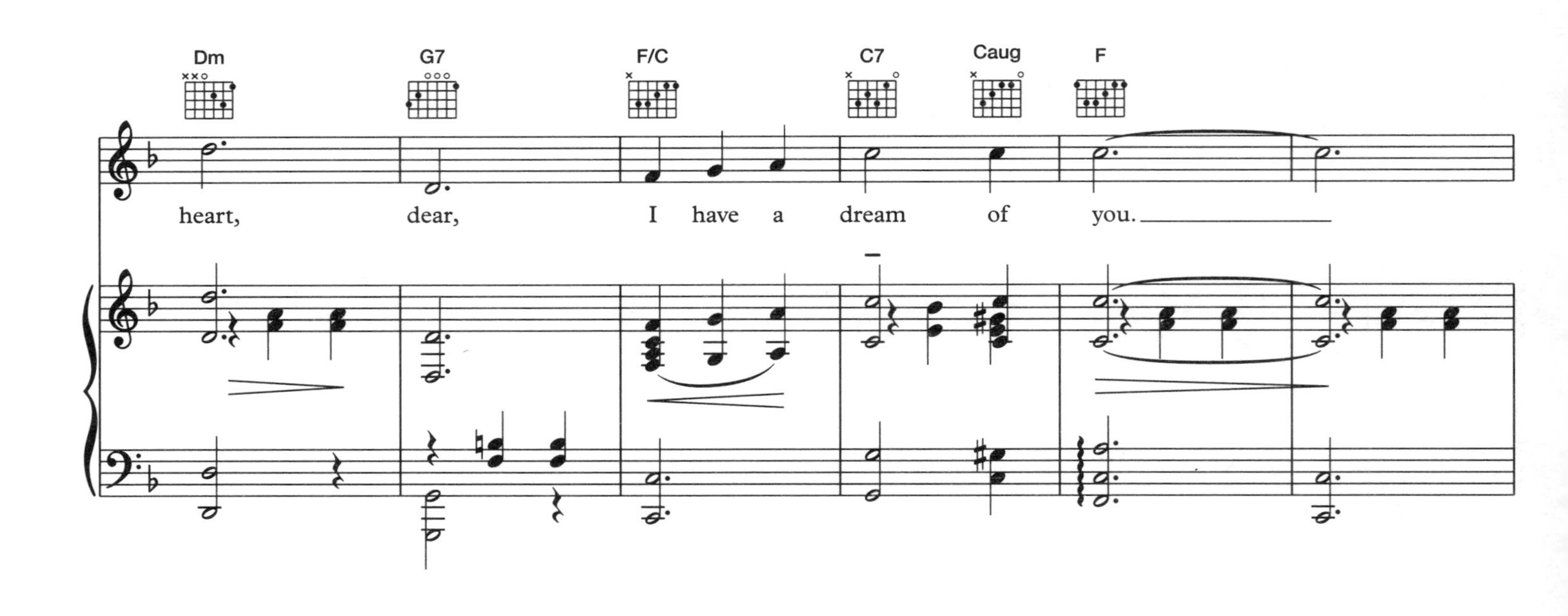
Dm
G7
F/C
C7
Caug
F
heart, dear, I have a dream of you.

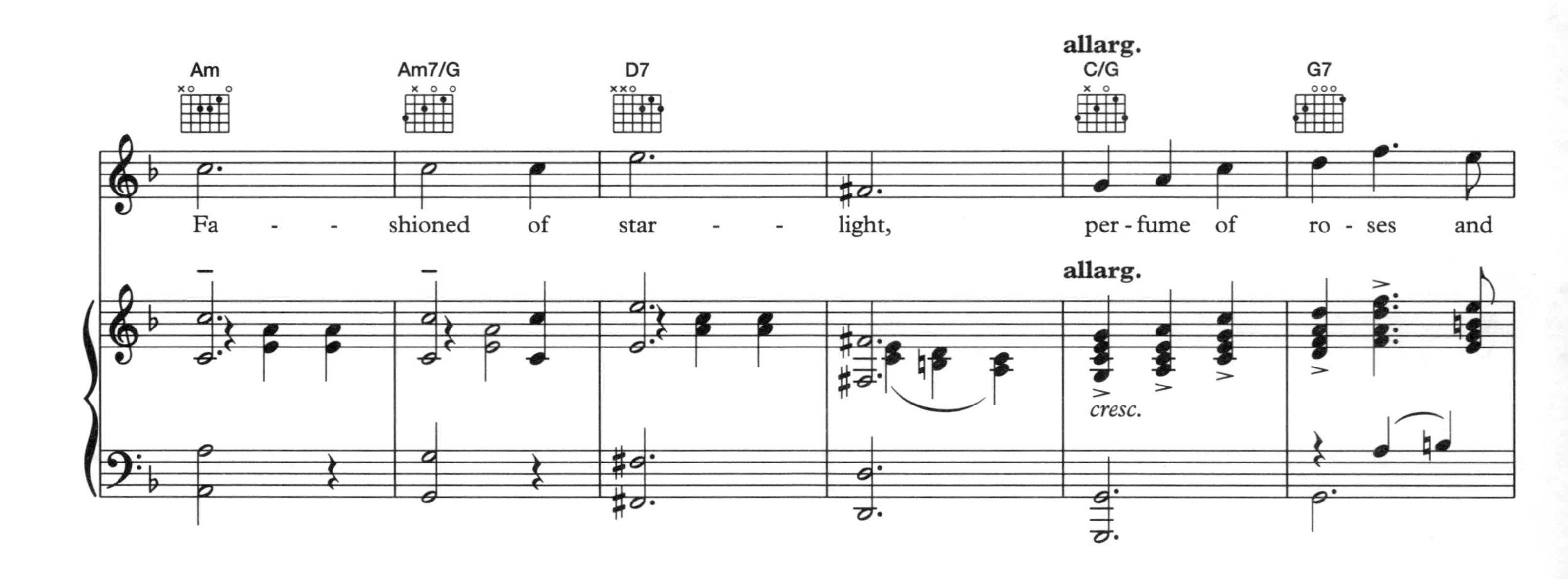
Am
Am7/G
D7
allarg.
C/G
G7
Fa - - shioned of star - - light, per - fume of ro - ses and
allarg.
cresc.

poco rit.
a tempo
C7
Dm
B♭
F/A
D7
dew.
Our paths may sev - - er,
mf
rit.
rall.
molto allarg.
Gm
3fr
G7
Caug
F
A7/E
but I'll re - mem - ber for ev - - er,
(Both)
deep in my
f
Dm
G7
F/C
C7
molto rall.
F
heart, dear, al - ways I'll dream of you!
8va
ff

THE DESERT SONG

Words by OTTO HARBACH and OSCAR HAMMERSTEIN II
Music by SIGMUND ROMBERG

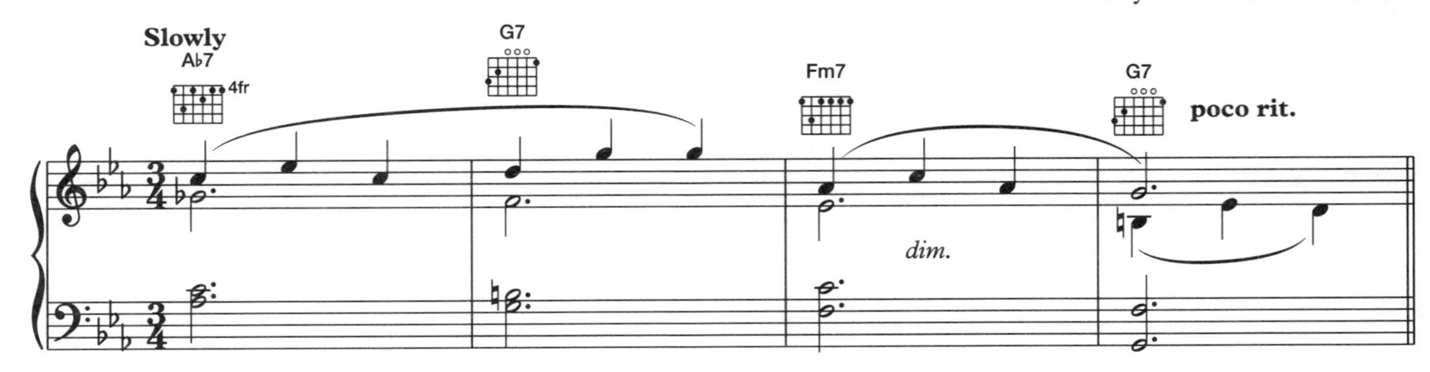

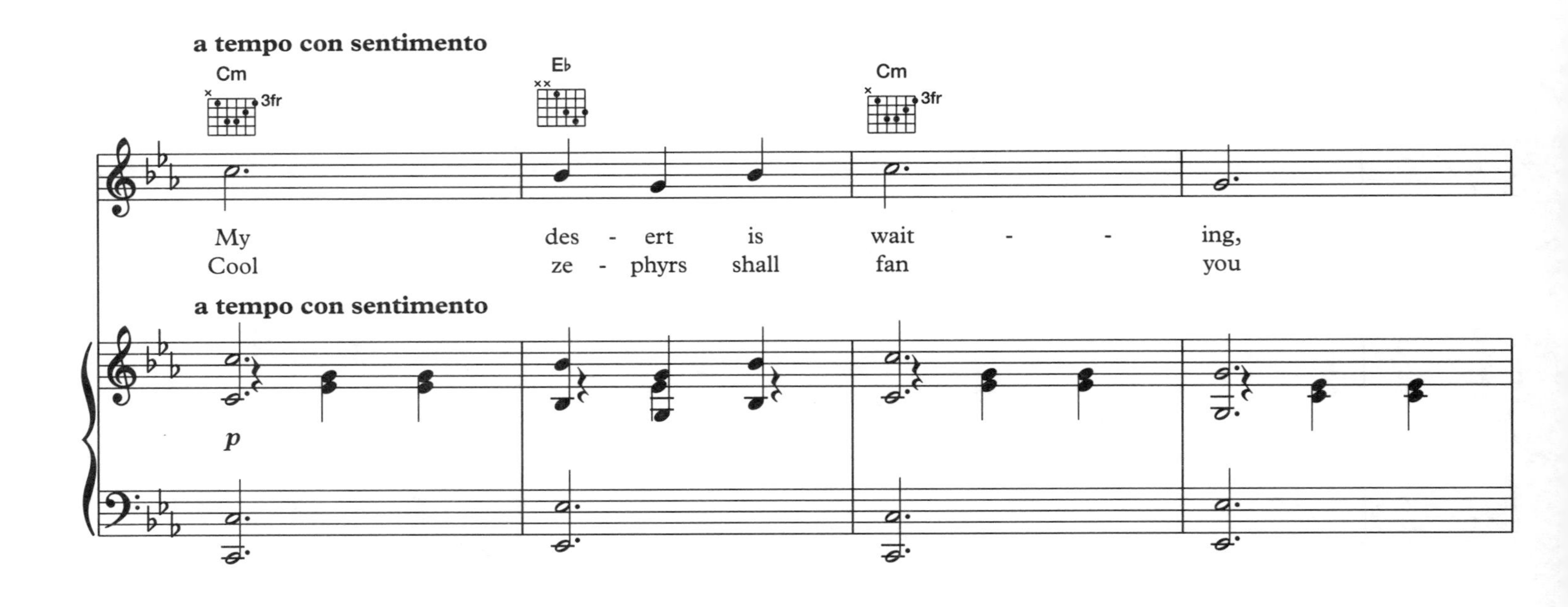

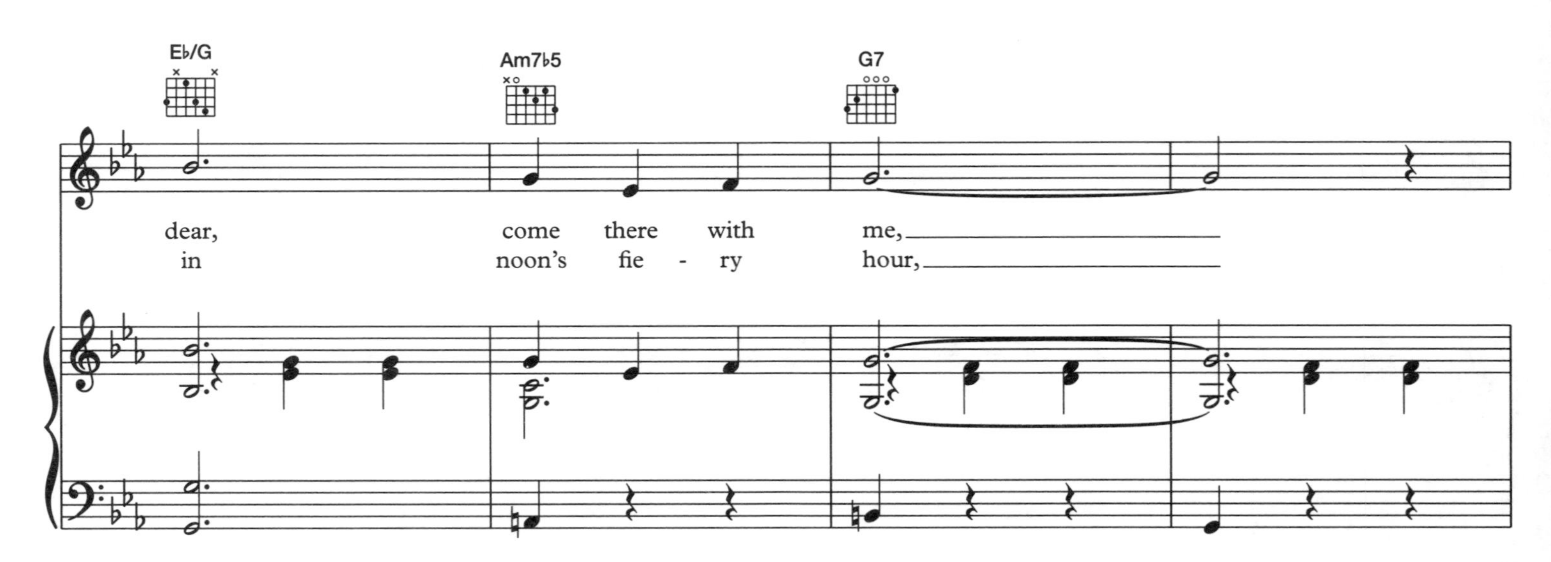

Cm
3fr
E♭
Cm
3fr
I'm long - ing to teach you
while sha - dy o - a - - ses
G
D7
G
love's sweet me - lo - dy.
we'll seek for a bower.
E♭
G7
I'll sing a dream - song to you,
Al - lah sends gifts from a - bove,
E♭
G7
poco rall.
G7♯5
paint - ing a pic - ture for two.
gives you my life and my love.
poco rall.

a tempo
C
Gaug
Dm
G7
Blue heaven, and you and I, and
a tempo
p-mf
Dm7
G7
Cmaj7
C
sand kissing a moonlit sky. A desert
E7
Am
Cdim7
breeze whispering a lullaby, only
mf
R.H.
D6
D7
G9
poco rall.
G7
G7#5
a tempo
C
stars above you to see I love you. Oh,
poco rall.
a tempo
p-mf

Gaug
Dm
G7
Dm7
give me that night di - vine, and let
Cmaj7
C
my arms in yours en - twine. The des - ert song
E7
Am
D7/F#
C/G
call - ing, its voice en - thrall - ing will make you
mf
1.
2.
D.C.
mine.
mine.
sf

DINAH

Words by SAM LEWIS and JOE YOUNG
Music by HARRY AKST

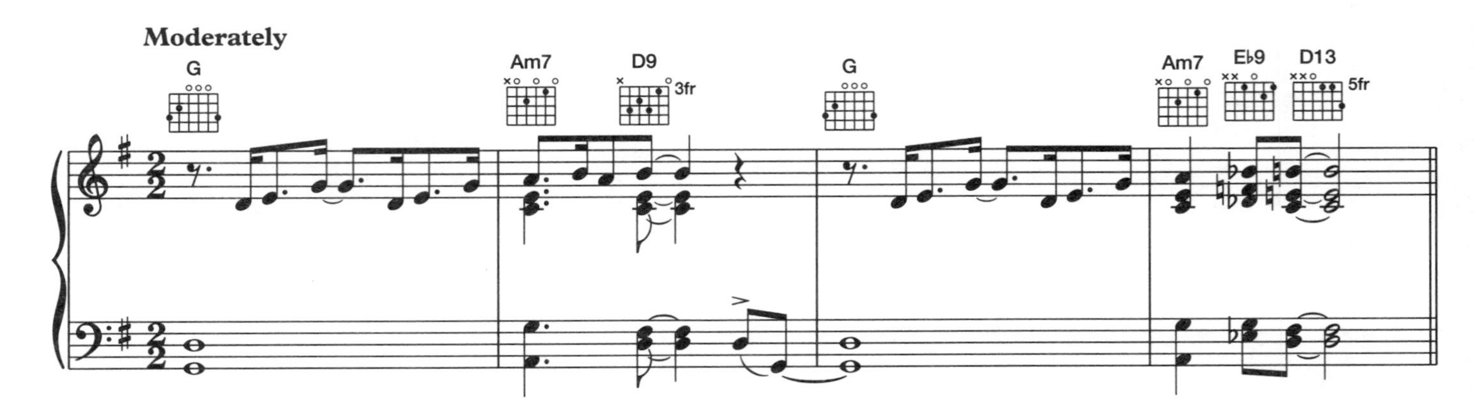

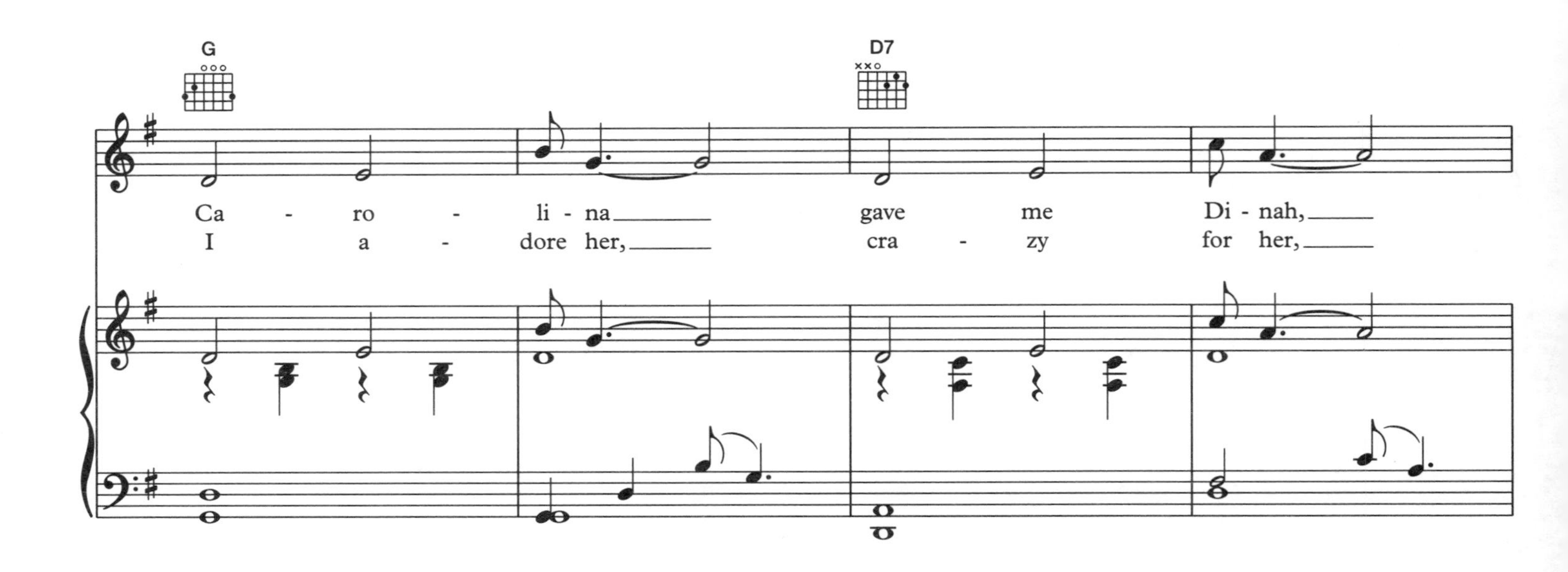

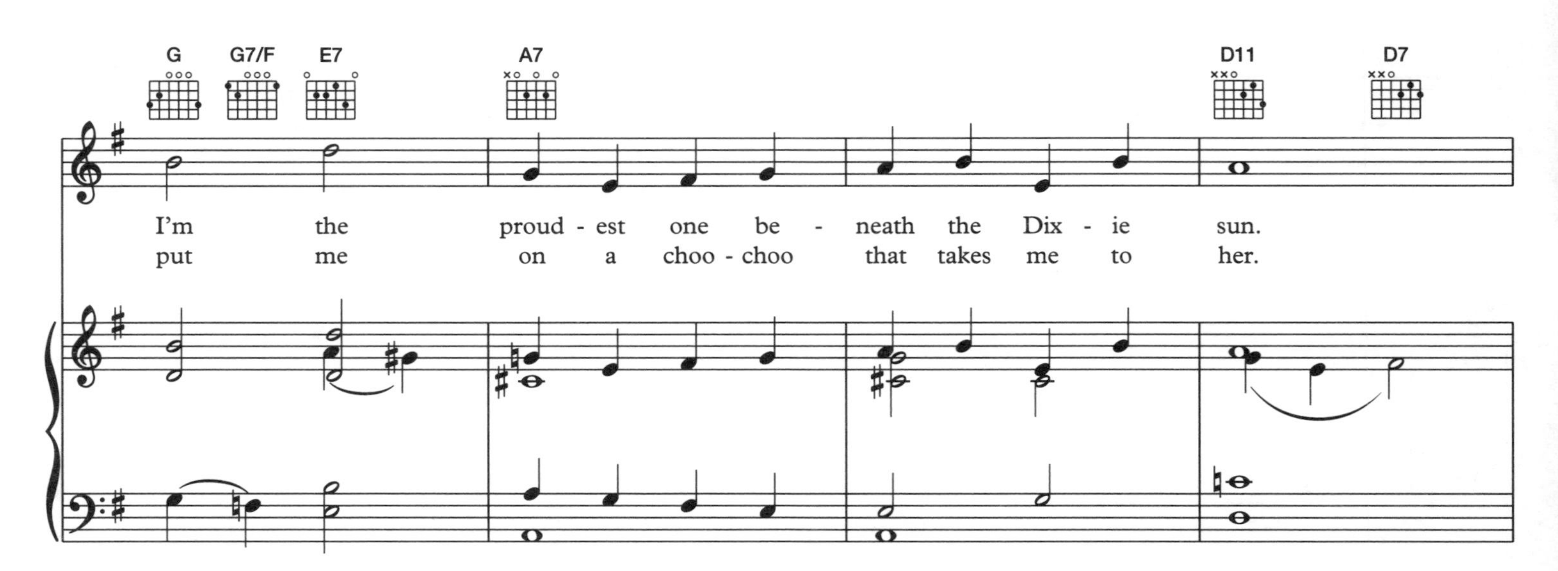

G
Bm
G7
News is spread-in' 'bout a wed-din',
How I wor-ry, jus' must hur-ry,
D
Bm
Em7
A7
D7
D7#5
I hear church bells ring-in', here's the song my heart keeps sing-in'.
I can't bear to lin-ger, I've a ring that needs a fin-ger.
G
Gmaj7
G
Di-nah, is there a-ny-one fi-ner in the state of Ca-ro-
Am7
D9/F#
D7
G
B♭dim7
-li-na? If there is, and you know 'er,

Am7
D7
G
show her to me!
Di - nah,
with her Dix - ie eyes
Gmaj7
G
Am7
blaz - in',
how I love to sit and gaze in - -
D9
3fr
D7
3fr
G
F6
F#6
G6
3fr
Cdim7
Em/B
B7/F#
- to the eyes of Di - nah Lee.
Em
Em(maj7)/G
Em7/G
Ev - ery night
why do I
shake with fright?

A7/G
D11
D7
Em
Em7/D
A7
Be - cause my Di - nah might change her mind a - bout
Am7
E♭9
D9
3fr
G
me.
Di - nah,
if she wan-dered to
Gmaj7
Chi - na,
I would hop an o - cean li - ner
just to be with Di - nah
1.
2.
Lee.
Lee.
A♭maj9
Gmaj9
D.C.

DON'T BRING LULU

Words by BILLY ROSE and LEW BROWN
Music by RAY HENDERSON

C7 F7 B♭ B♭/D D♭dim7
London Bridge is falling down. You can bring cake, or fil-lets of steak, but don't bring
F7 Cm/E♭ D7
Lu-lu. Lu-lu gets blue, and she goes 'cuck-oo', like the clock up-on the shelf.
E♭ E♭m B♭ G7 D♭dim7 F9/C B♭
rall.
She's the kind of smar-ty who breaks up ev-ery par-ty, hul-la-ba-loo-loo,
rall.
C7 B♭/F Gm Cm7 F7 B♭ F7 B♭
1.
2.
don't bring Lu-lu, I'll bring her my-self. Now -self.

FASCINATING RHYTHM

Music and Lyrics by
GEORGE GERSHWIN and IRA GERSHWIN

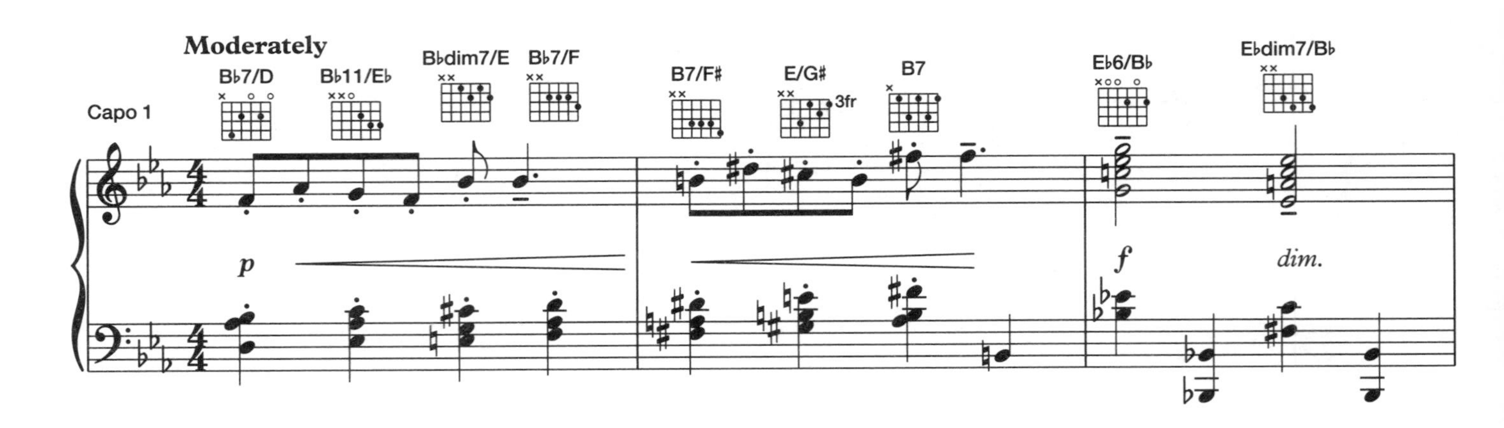

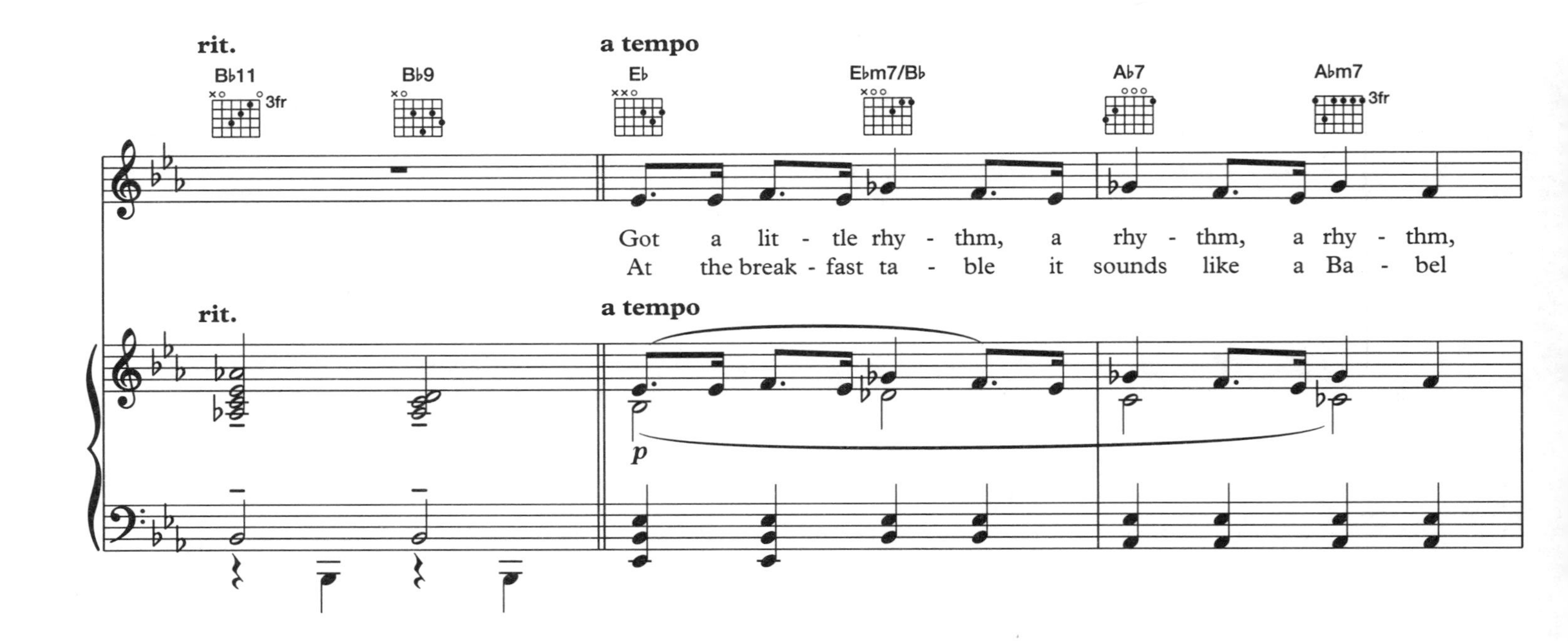

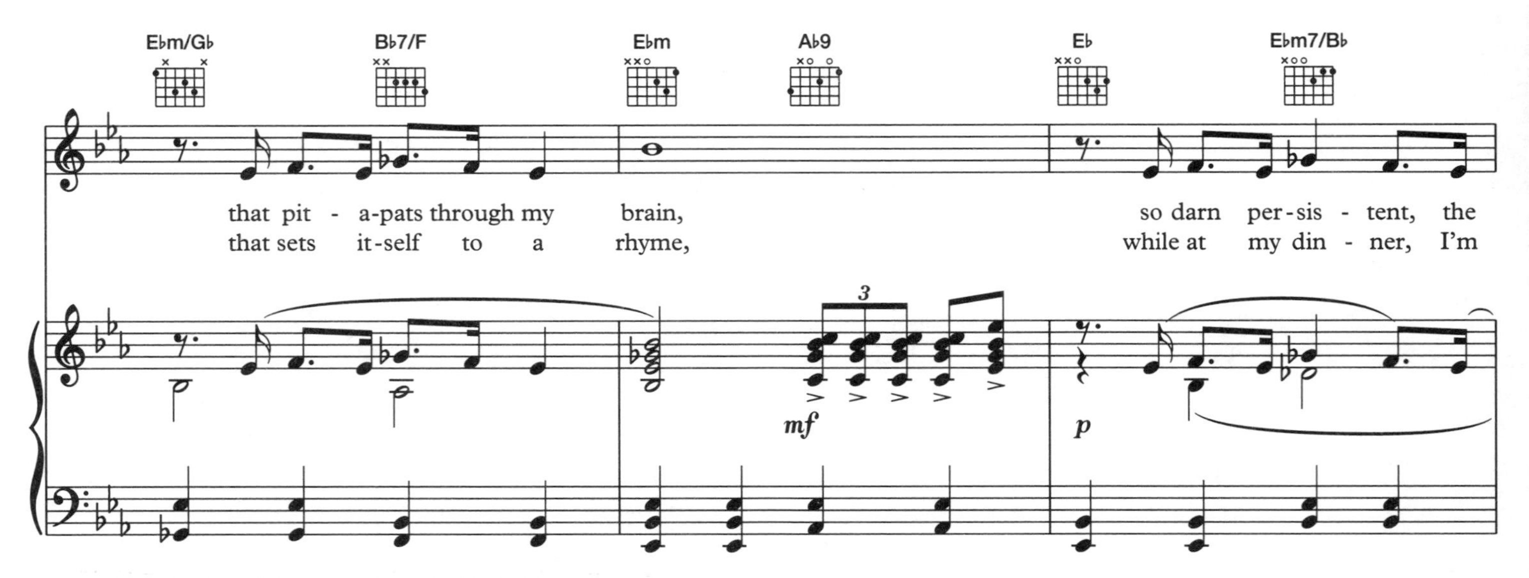

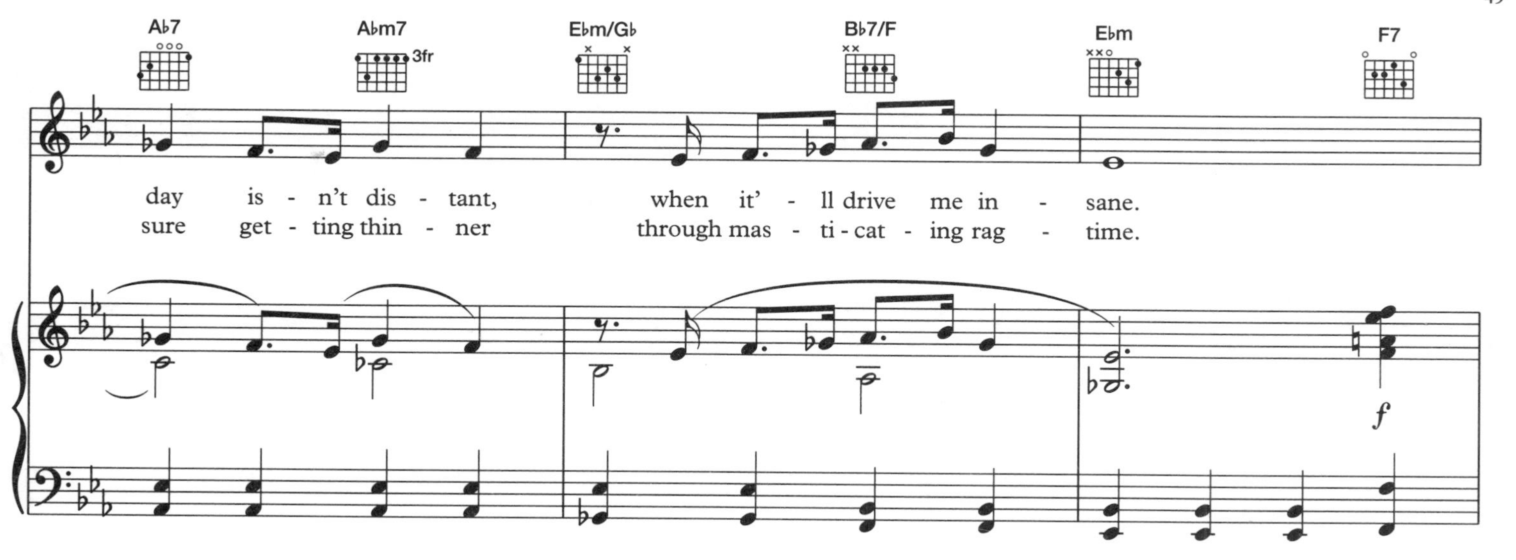
A♭7
A♭m7
3fr
E♭m/G♭
B♭7/F
E♭m
F7
day is - n't dis - tant, when it' - ll drive me in - sane.
sure get - ting thin - ner through mas - ti - cat - ing rag - time.
f

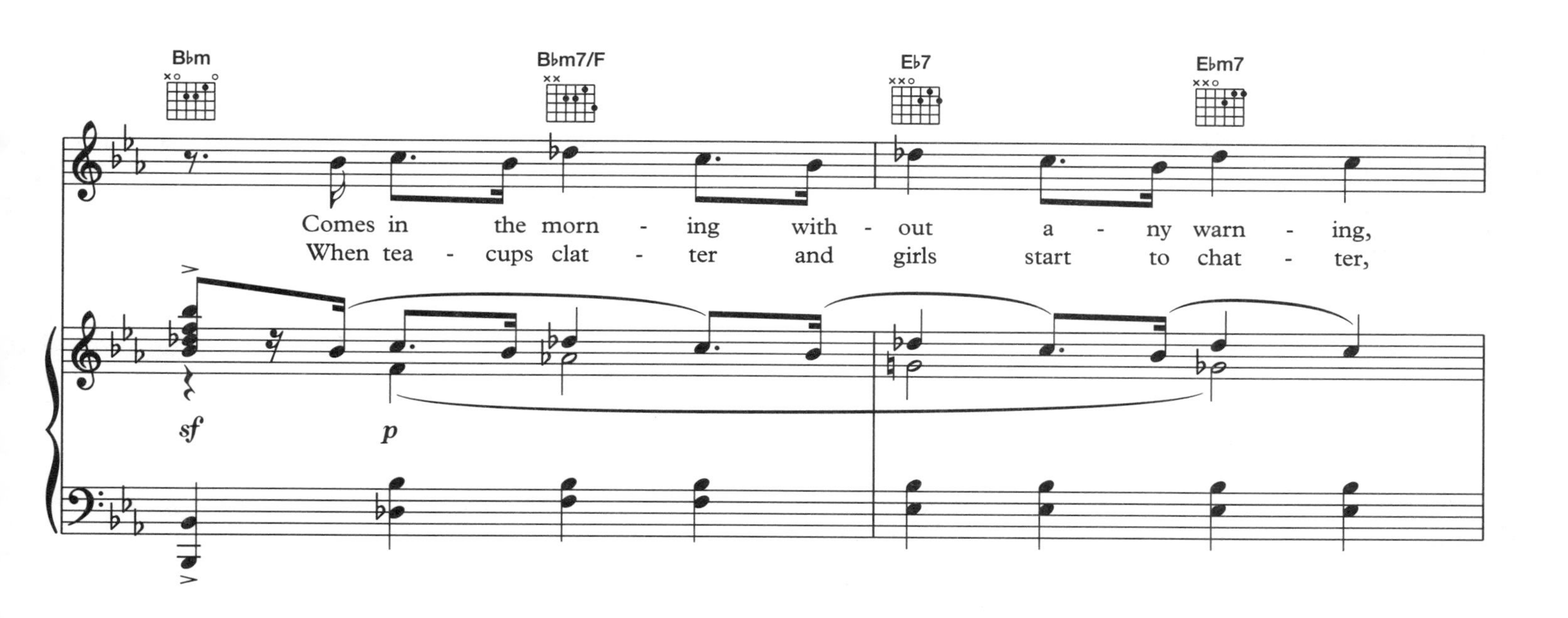
B♭m
B♭m7/F
E♭7
E♭m7
Comes in the morn - ing with - out a - ny warn - ing,
When tea - cups clat - ter and girls start to chat - ter,
sf
p

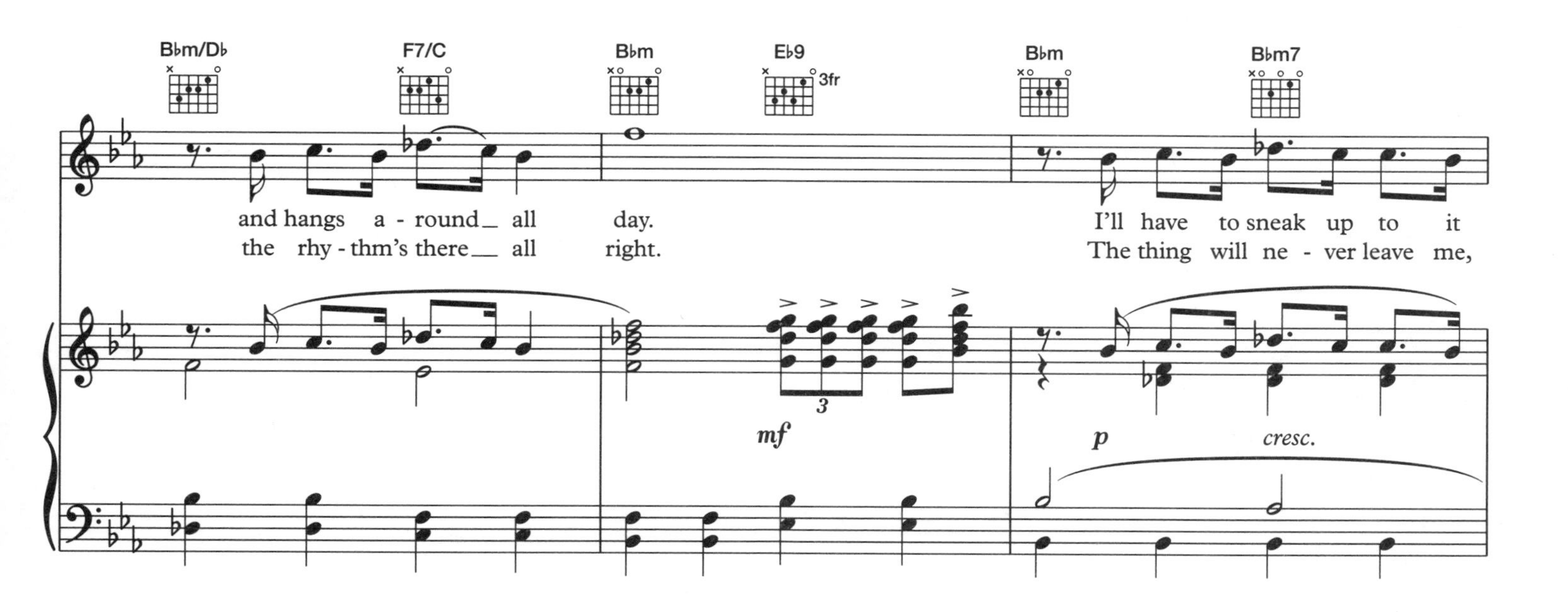
B♭m/D♭
F7/C
B♭m
E♭9
3fr
B♭m
B♭m7
and hangs a - round_ all day.
the rhy - thm's there_ all right.
I'll have to sneak up to it
The thing will ne - ver leave me,
mf
p
cresc.

E♭7/B♭ E♭m7/B♭ F7 B♭
3fr
some-day, and speak up to it, I hope it lis - tens when I say:
why, when in bed, be-lieve me, as soon as I blow out the light:
B♭7/D B♭11/E♭ B♭7/F B♭11/E♭ B♭7/D B♭11/E♭ B♭7/F B♭11/E♭ B♭7/D B♭11/E♭ B♭7/F B♭11/E♭
Fas - ci - nat - ing rhy-thm, you've got me on the go! Fas - ci - nat - ing rhy-thm, I'm all a -
B♭7 E♭7/G E♭11/A♭ E♭7/B♭ E♭11/A♭ E♭7/G E♭11/A♭ E♭7/B♭ E♭11/A♭
- qui - ver. What a mess you're mak-ing! The neigh-bours want to know why I'm
E♭7/G E♭11/A♭ E♭7/B♭ E♭11/A♭ E♭7 A♭ A♭/G
al - ways shak-ing, just like a fliv - ver. Each morn - ing

Fm7 B♭6 B♭9♯5 E♭ Cm Cm7
I get up with the sun, (start a-hop-ping, ne-ver stop-ping), to find at
Cm7 Cm7♭5 F F13♭9 B♭7 C♯dim7
night no work has been done. I know that
B♭7/D B♭11/E♭ B♭7/F B♭11/E♭ B♭7/D B♭11/E♭ B♭7/F B♭11/E♭ B♭7/D B♭11/E♭ B♭7/F B♭11/E♭
once it did-n't mat-ter, but now you're do-ing wrong when you start to pat-ter, I'm so un-
B♭7 E♭7/G E♭11/A♭ E♭7/B♭ E♭11/A♭ E♭7/G E♭11/A♭ E♭7/B♭ E♭11/A♭
-hap-py. Won't you take a day off, de-cide to run a-long some-where

E♭7/G E♭11/A♭ E♭7/B♭ E♭11/A♭ E♭7 A♭ Dm7♭5 G7
3fr
far a-way off, and make it snap - py? Oh, how I long to be the man
mf
Cm Cm9/B♭ F7/A B♭7/D B♭11/E♭ B♭7/F B♭11/E♭
I used to be! Fas - ci - nat - ing rhy - thm, oh,
p
B♭7/D F7/C B♭13
1.
E♭ E/G♯ D/F♯ C/E B/D♯
3fr
4fr
won't you stop pick - ing on me?
2.
E♭ A♭maj7 Cm7 E♭maj7 Fm7 A♭maj7 E♭
D.C.
me!
mf
cresc.
sf

GIRL OF MY DREAMS

Words and Music by SUNNY CLAPP

E/B
B7/F♯
Gdim7
B7
E
B/D♯
4fr
G7
-ed, try - ing so hard to for - get.
you, sweet - heart, in me - mo - ry lane.
Girl of my
C
G7/D
C7/E
F
Dm7♭5
C/G
dreams, I love you, hon - est I do, you
p-f
Gaug
C
Gaug
C
G7/D
C7/E
Caug
are so sweet. If I could just hold your charms a -
F
A♭7/G♭
C/G
D7
G7
C
-gain in my arms, then life would be com - plete.

E7
Am
Am7
— Since you've been gone dear, life don't seem the same.
D7
G7
Fm6/A♭
3fr
G7
C
G7/D
Please come back a - gain, and af - ter all's said and
C7/E
F
A♭7
4fr
C/G
D7
G7
done, there's on - ly one, girl of my dreams, it's
1.
C
E♭dim7
Dm7
G7
you. Girl of my
2.
C
E♭9
F9
C
D.C.
you.

HAPPY DAYS AND LONELY NIGHTS

Words by BILLY ROSE
Music by FRED FISHER

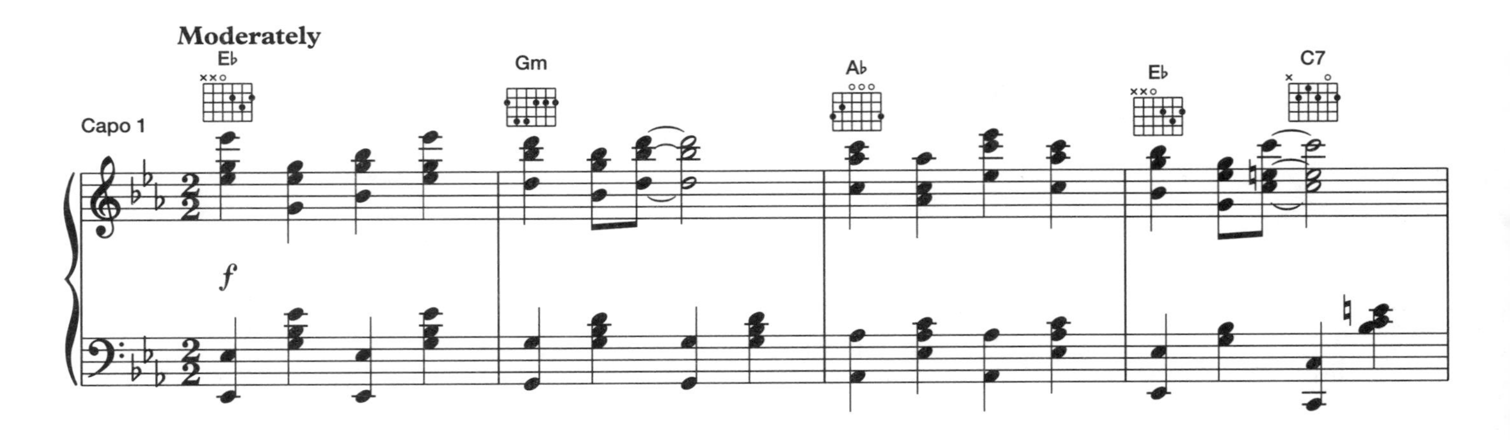

E♭
B♭7
D7/C
E♭
nights we knew, when I made love to you un - til the dawn.
sad and grey, oh, how I hate the day I let you go.
F7
B♭7
E♭
You left, and to my sur - prise, I'm laugh - ing with tear-dimmed eyes,
I find that my hap - pi - ness de - pends on your sweet ca - ress,
Cm
F7
B♭
F7
B♭
be - cause I re - al - ize I can't go on, my dar - ling.
I thought I loved you less, but now I know, my dar - ling.

E♭ Gm A♭ E♭ C7
With the part - ing of the ways, you took all my hap - py days,
p–f
F7 B♭11 3fr B♭7 E♭ F7 B♭7 E♭
and left me lone - ly nights.
Morn-ing ne - ver
Gm A♭ E♭ C7 F7
comes too soon, I can face the af - ter - noon, but oh, those
B♭11 3fr B♭7 E♭ E♭7 A♭ G7
lone - ly nights.
I feel your arms a - round me, your

C7
F7
kiss - es lin - ger yet, you taught me how to love you, now
F7#5
B♭7
B♭7#5
E♭
Gm
teach me to for - get! You broke my heart a mil - lion ways
A♭
E♭
C7
F7
B♭11
3fr
B♭7
when you took my hap - py days, and left me lone - ly
1.
E♭
C7/G
G♭dim7
B♭7/F
2.
E♭
D.𝄋
nights.
nights.

I BELONG TO GLASGOW

Words and Music by WILL FYFFE

Moderately

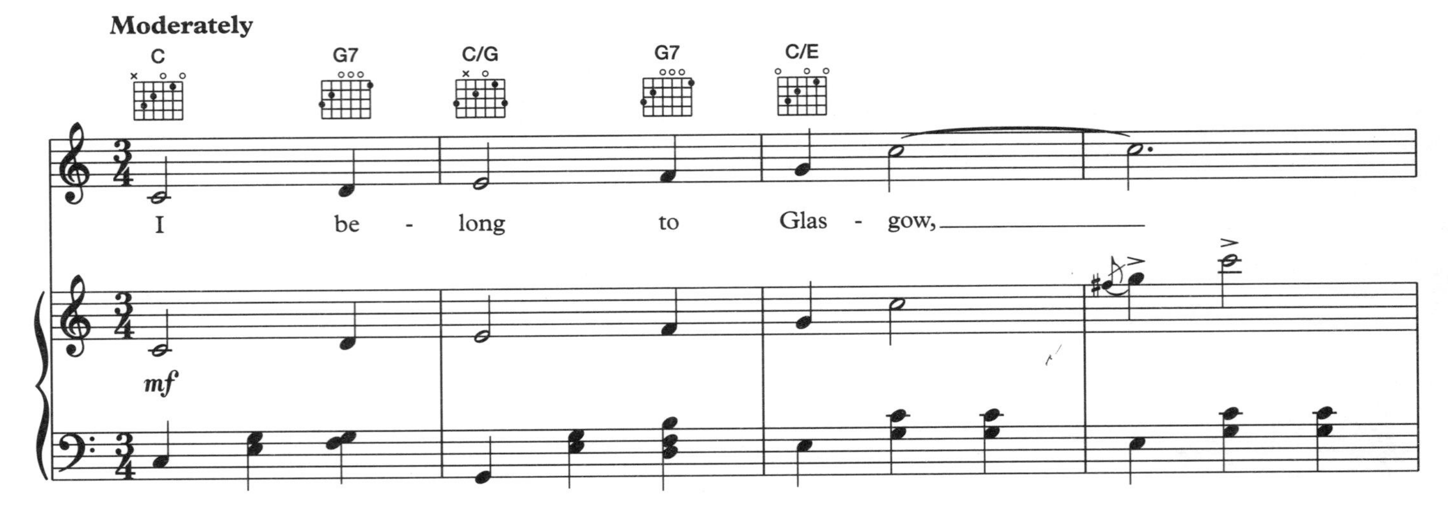

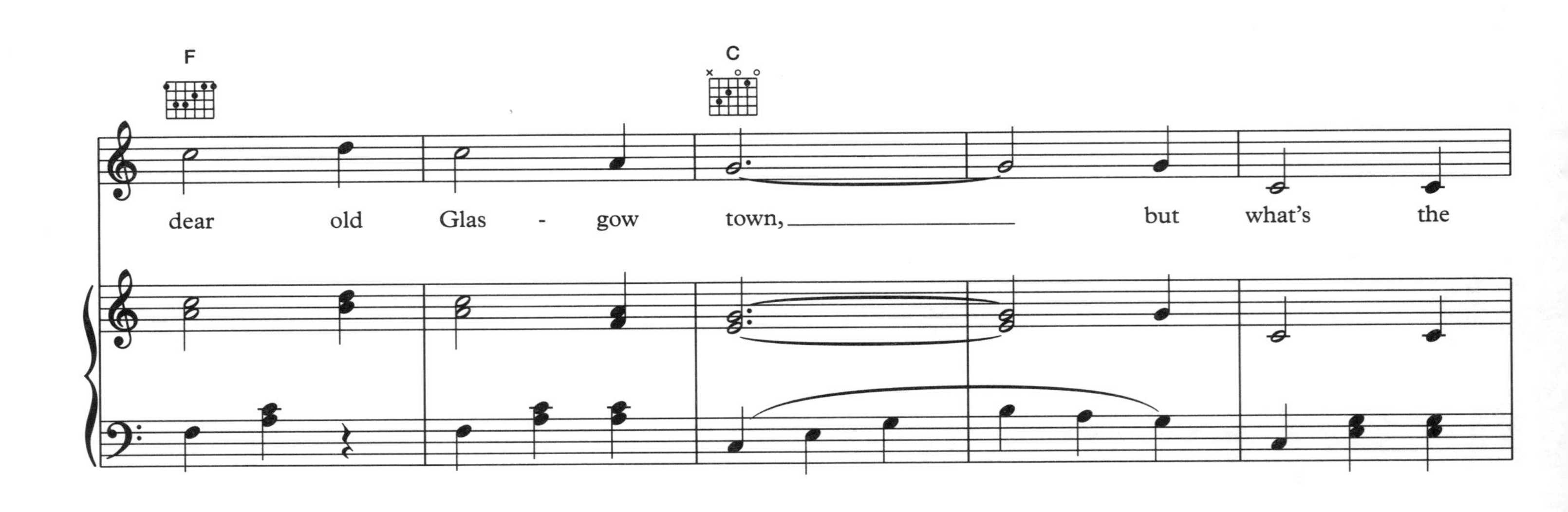

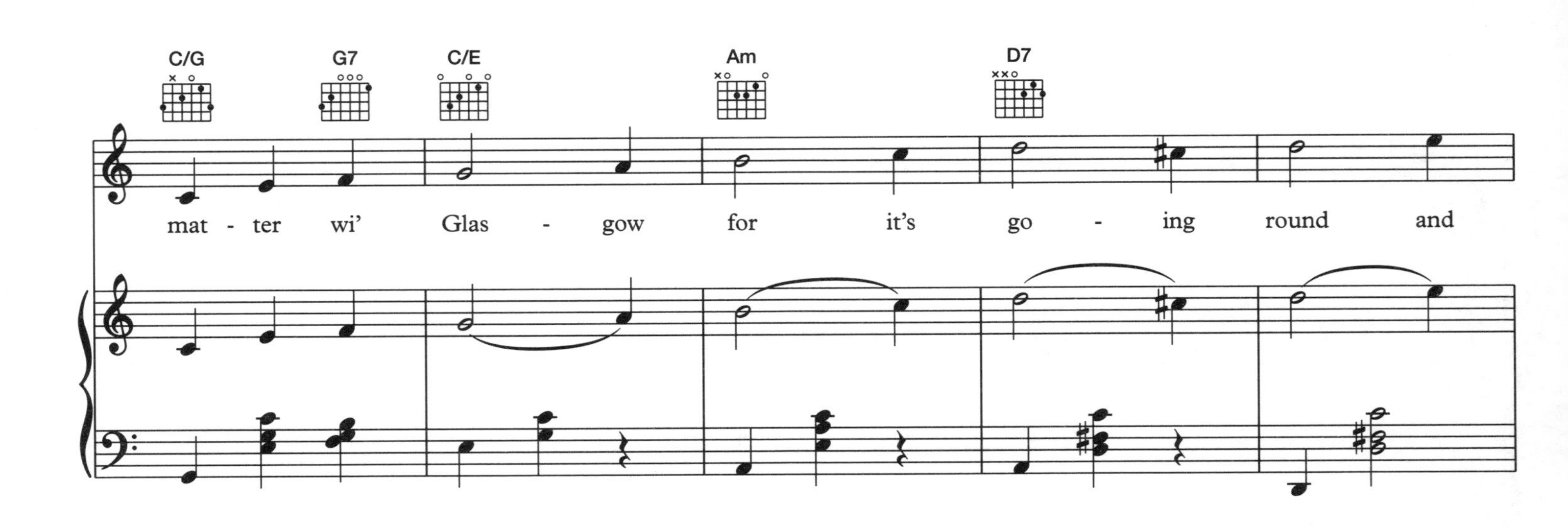

G7
C/E
G7/D
C
G7/D
C/E
round?
I'm on - ly a com - mon old
D7
G11
G7/B
F
C
D7
work - ing chap, as a - ny - one can see,
G7
C
Dm7
D#dim7
C/E
F
C/E
F
C/E
but when I get a cou - ple of drinks on a
A7
D7
INTRO!
G7
C
D.C.
Sa - tur - day, Glas - gow be - longs to me!
sfz

I CAN'T GIVE YOU ANYTHING BUT LOVE

Words by DOROTHY FIELDS
Music by JIMMY McHUGH

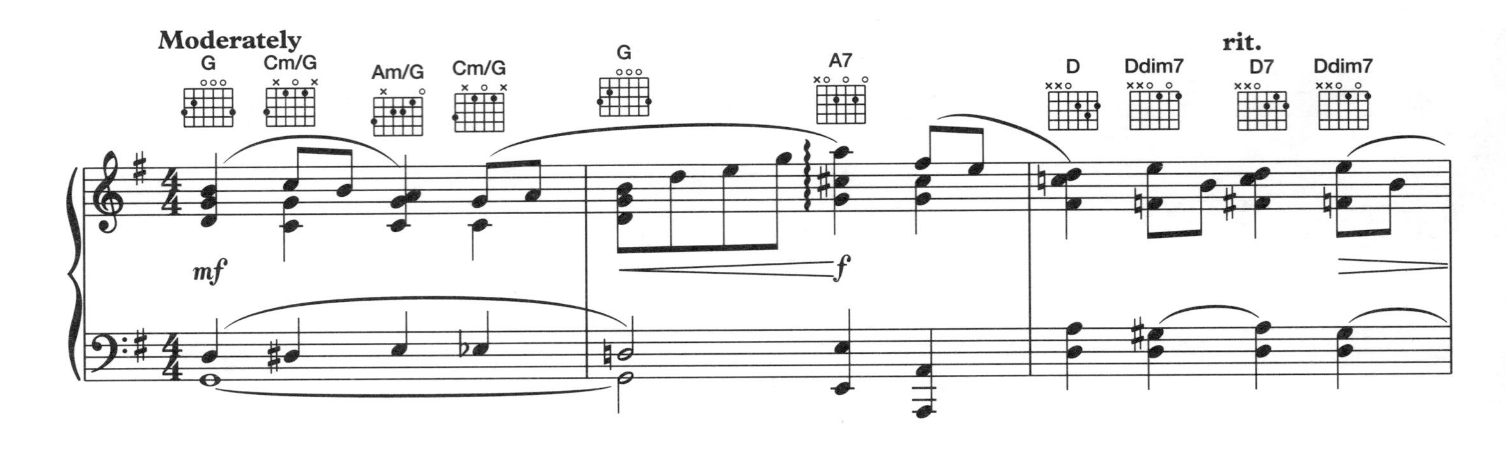

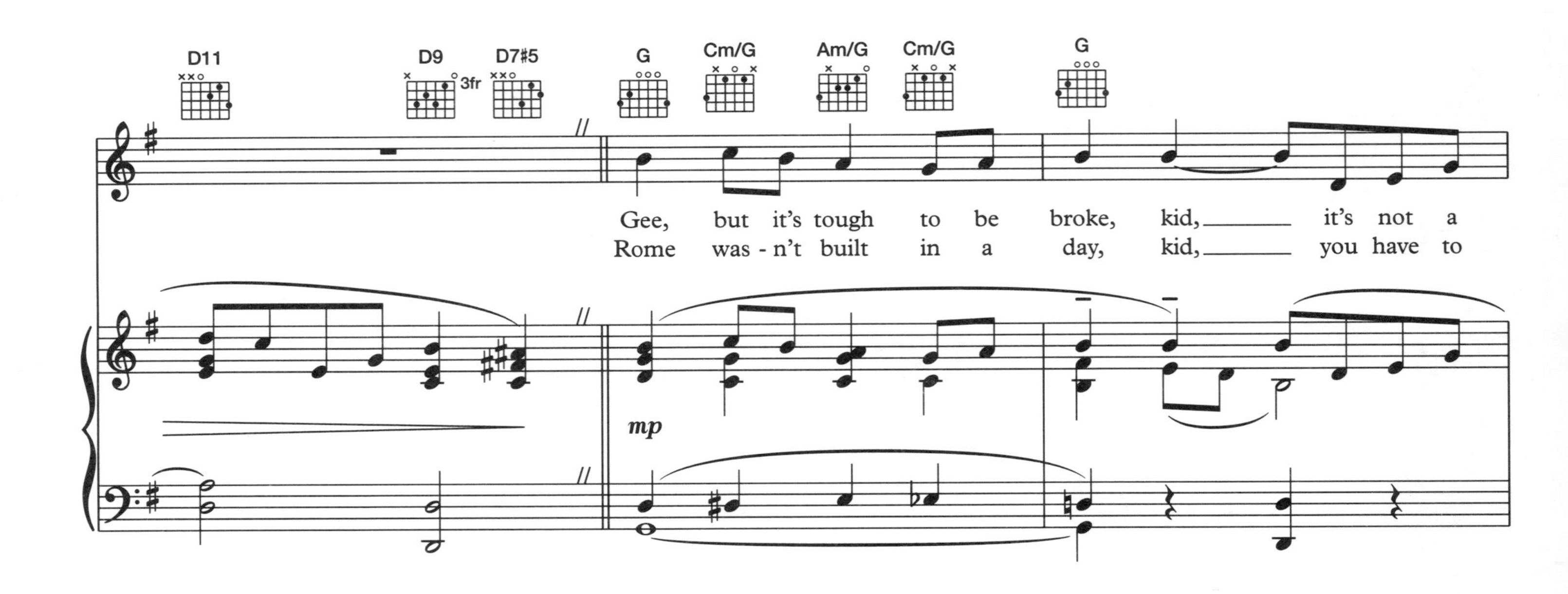

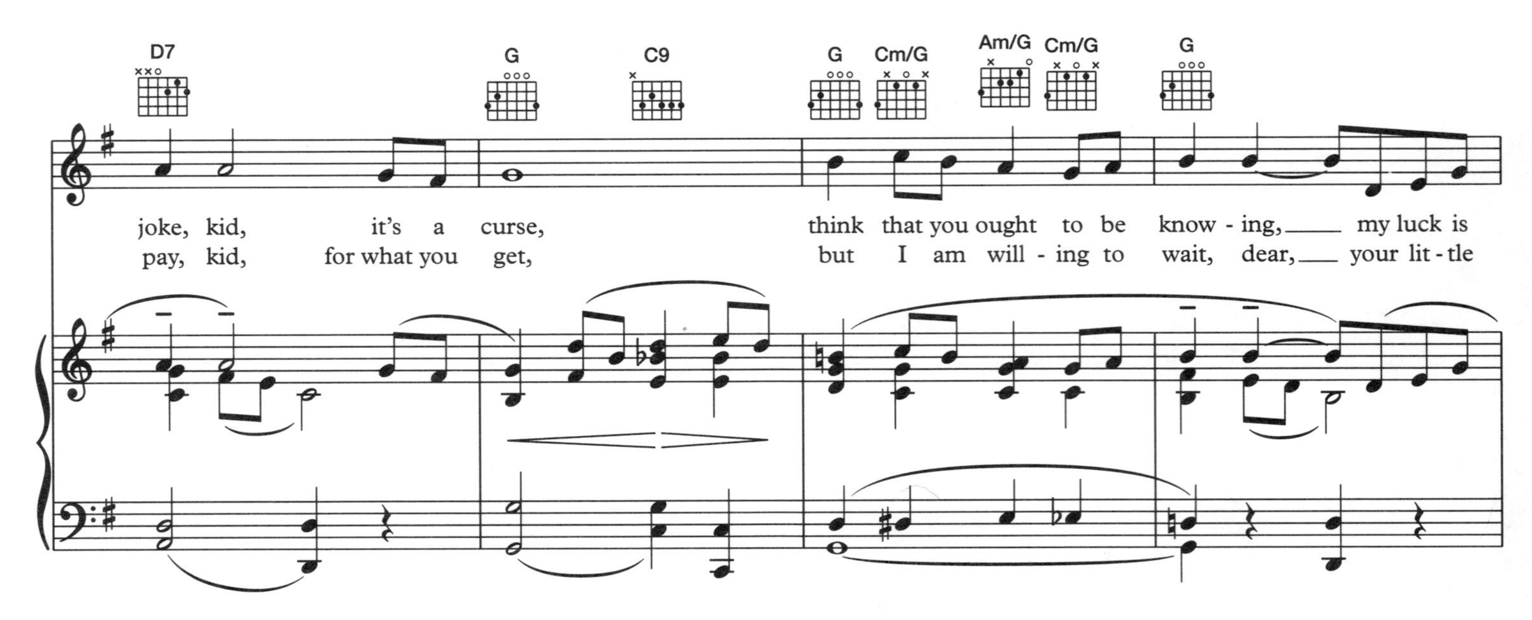

D7
G
G7
Bm
F#
go - ing from bad to worse.
Who knows, some-day I will
mate, dear, will not for - get.
You have a life - time be -
E9
E7
E/B
B♭dim7
Am7
Cm/G
Am/G
win too, I'll be - gin to reach my prime?
Now, though I see what our
- fore you, I'll a - dore you, come what may.
Please don't be blue for the
A7
poco rall.
D11
end is, all I can spend is just my time.
pre - sent, when it's so plea - sant to hear you say:

G
B♭dim7
Am7
D7
I can't give you a - ny - thing but love, ba - by,
mp–f
G
A7
D11
D7
that's the on - ly thing I've plen - ty of, ba - by.
G7
C
B
B♭
Dream a-while, scheme a-while, we're sure to find
A7
rit.
D7
B♭7
A♭7
4fr
C7
D7
hap - pi-ness, and I guess all those things you've al - ways pined for.
rit.

G
a tempo
B♭dim7
Am7
D7
Gee, I'd like to see you look - ing swell, ba - by,
a tempo
G7
Cmaj7
C
dia-mond brace-lets Wool-worth does - n't sell, ba - by. Till that luc - ky
A7/E
E♭7
G/D
E7
Am7
rit.
A9/D
D13
3fr
5fr
day you know darned well, ba - by, I can't give you a - ny - thing but
rit.
1.
a tempo
G
B♭dim7
Am7
D7
2.
allarg.
G
Am7♭5
G
D.C.
love.
love.
a tempo
allarg.
fz

I'LL BE WITH YOU IN APPLE BLOSSOM TIME

Words by NEVILLE FLEESON
Music by ALBERT VON TILZER

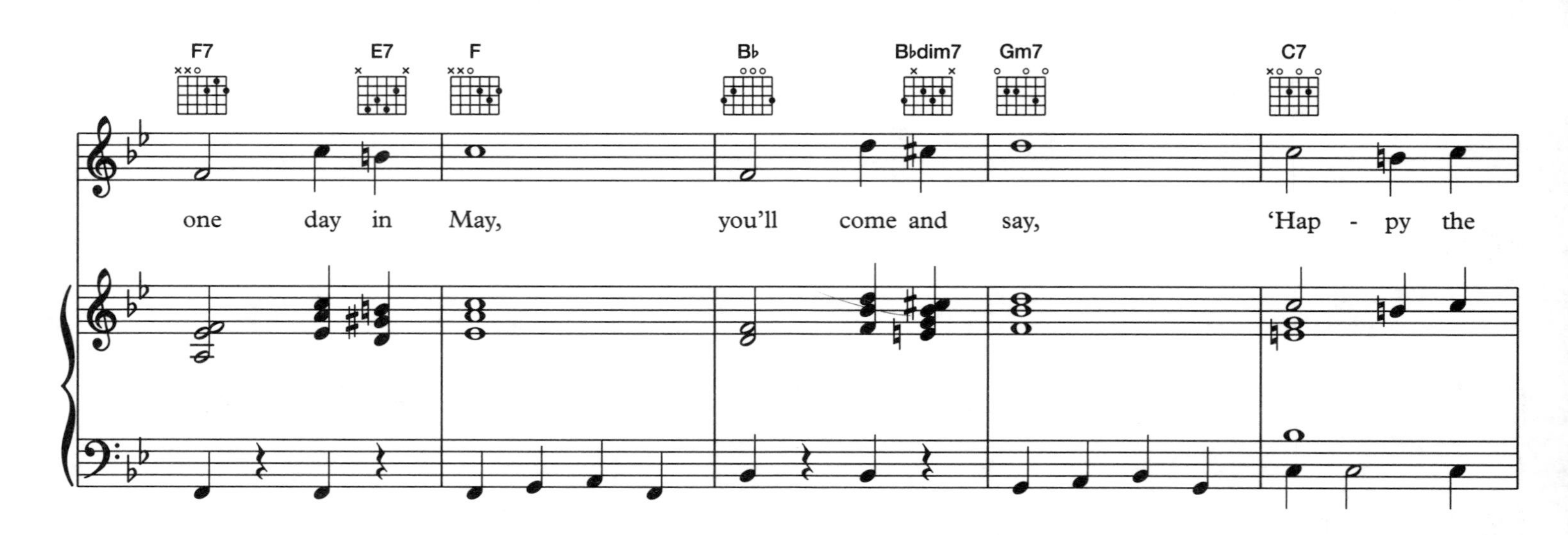

F Gdim7 G♯dim7 F7/A 3fr B♭
bride that the sun shines on to - day'. What a won - der - ful
Dm E♭ D7
wed - ding there will be, what a won - der - ful day for you and
G Gm7♭5 G7 C7
me, church bells will chime, you will be mine in
F11 F7 F11 F7 B♭
ap - ple blos - som time.

IF YOU KNEW SUSIE

Words by BUDDY DE SYLVA
Music by JOSEPH MEYER

C
Em
Em(maj7)
wow,
though all of you
spree,
no - bo - dy knows
Em
A7
G/D
D7
may know her too,
I'd like to shout right
where Su - sie goes,
no - bo - dy knows but
G
C
now.
If you knew Su - sie, like
me.
If you knew Su - sie, like
p-f
C#dim7
3fr
I know Su - sie, oh, oh,
I know Su - sie, oh, oh,

G7
oh what a girl! There's none so clas - sy as
oh what a girl! She wears long tress - es, and
this fair las - sie, oh, oh,
nice tight dress - es, oh, oh,
Gaug
C
D7
G7
C7
ho - ly Mo - ses what a chas - sis! We went rid - ing,
what a fu - ture she pos - ses - ses! Out in pub - lic,
F
D7
she did - n't balk from the coun - try,
how she can yawn in a par - lour,

G7
C
I'm the one that had to walk! If you knew Su - sie, like
you would think the war was on, If you knew Su - sie, like

D7
Fm6
G7
I know Su - sie, oh, oh, what a girl!
I know Su - sie, oh, oh what a girl!

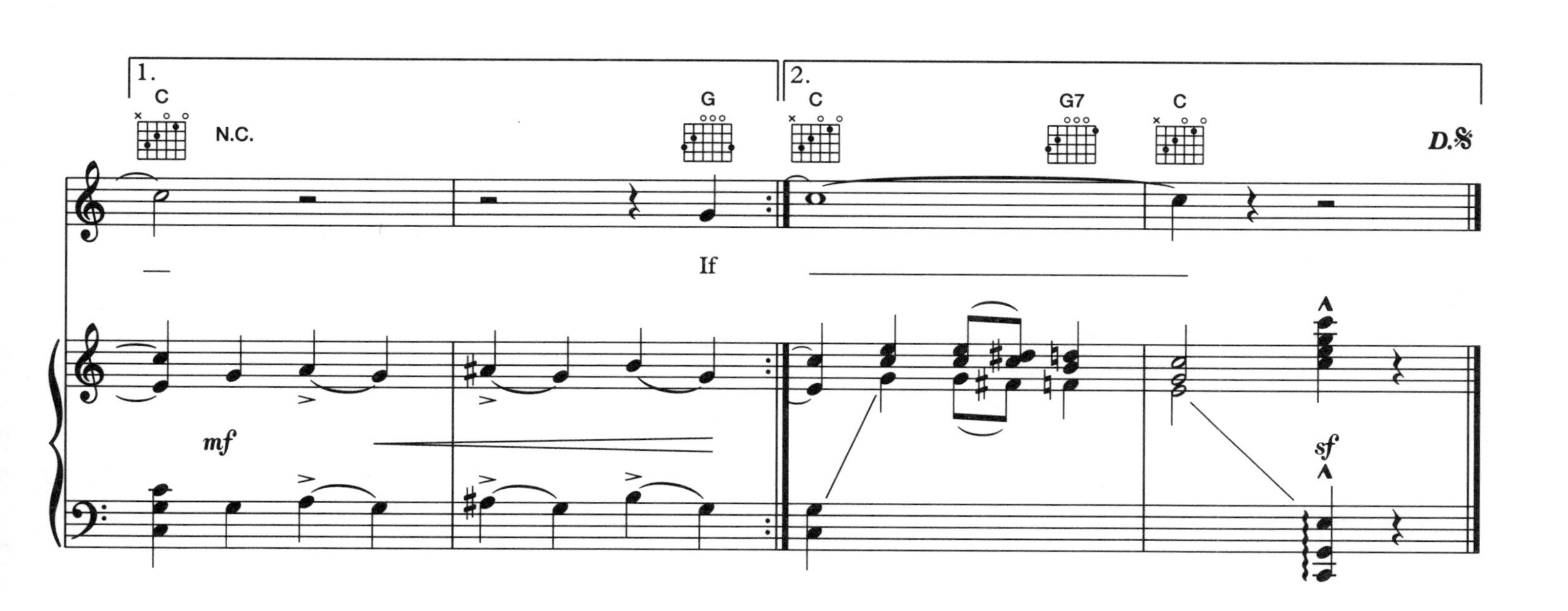
1.
C
N.C.
G
2.
C
G7
C
D.𝄋
If
mf
sf

IT HAD TO BE YOU

Words by GUS KAHN
Music by ISHAM JONES

Moderately

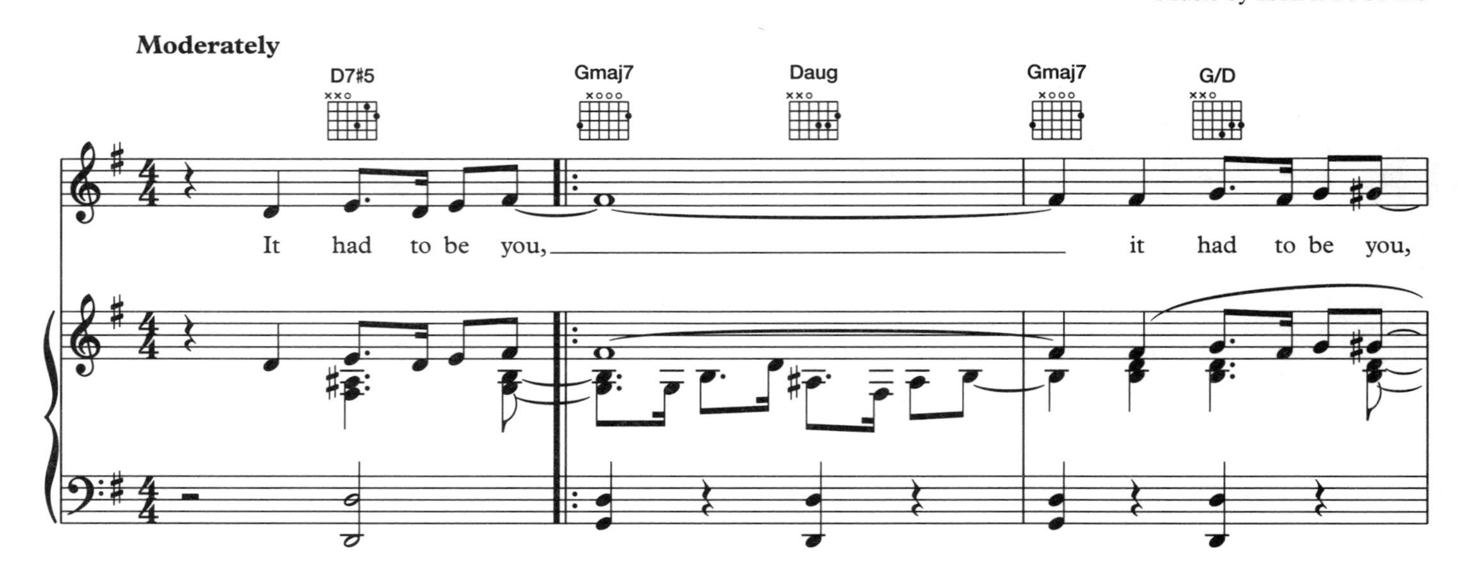

D♯dim
Em
could make me be blue,
and ev - en be glad
A7
D9
E♭9♭5
D9
just to be sad,
think - ing of you.
Daug
Gmaj7
Daug
Gmaj7
G/D
Some oth - ers I've seen
might ne - ver be mean,
E7
A7
might ne - ver be cross,
or try to be boss,

N.C.
but they would-n't do,
for no-bo-dy else
Am
Am7/G
F#dim7
D7
G
B7
gave me a thrill,
with all your faults,
I love you still.
Em
Bm
B♭dim7
D7
B♭dim7
D7
It had to be you,
won-der-ful you,
had to be you.
1.
G
B♭dim7
Am7♭5
D7
Daug
2.
G
Cm6
G6
It had to be you.

MISTAKES

Words by EDGAR LESLIE
Music by EVERETT LYNTON

E7
Am
G/D
D7
G7
Gaug
I'll make a - mends, if you will just for - give me.
were things re - versed, I'd be the first to help you.
C
Cdim7
G7
We make mis - takes when we wor - - ry all o - ver
p–f
Dm
G7
E7
no - thing at all, we make mis - takes that bring
Am
D
A7/E
D7/F♯
D7
G7
heart - - aches, and the tear - - drops fall like rain - -

Gaug C Cdim7
-drops. We make mis - takes, and feel sor - - - ry
C7 F A7 F6
when we've made some - one blue, but I made the
F♯dim7 C/G E7/D A7 D7 Fm/A♭ G7
rit. a tempo
great - est mis - take of all when I said good - bye to
rit. a tempo
1. C E♭dim7 Dm7 G7
you.
2. C Fm/C C
you.
D.𝄋

THE MAN I LOVE

Music and Lyrics by
GEORGE GERSHWIN and IRA GERSHWIN

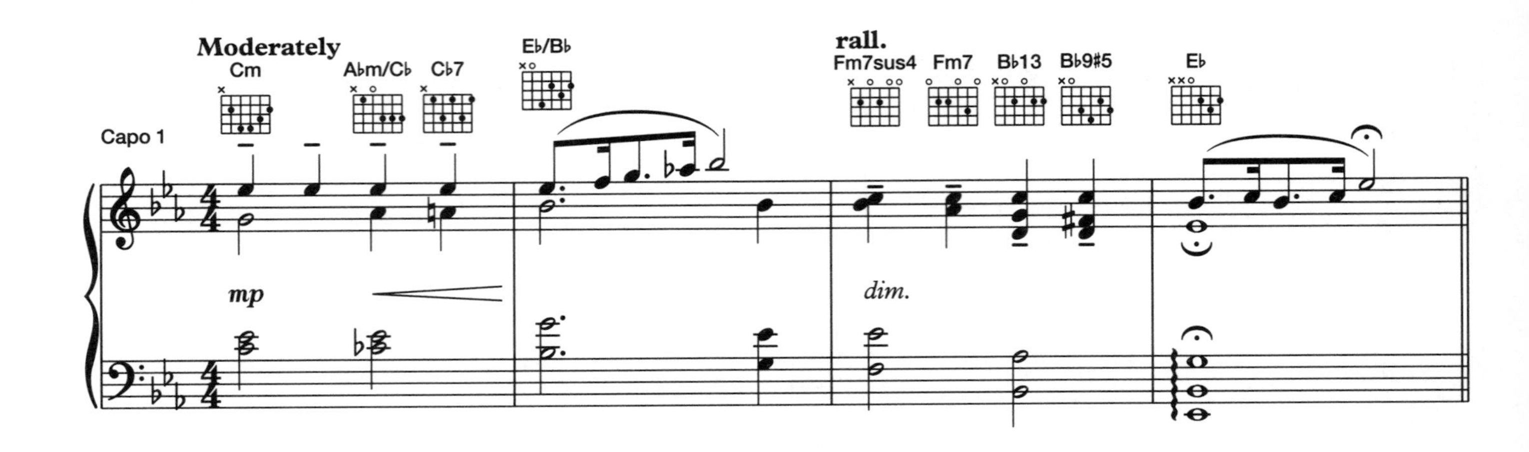

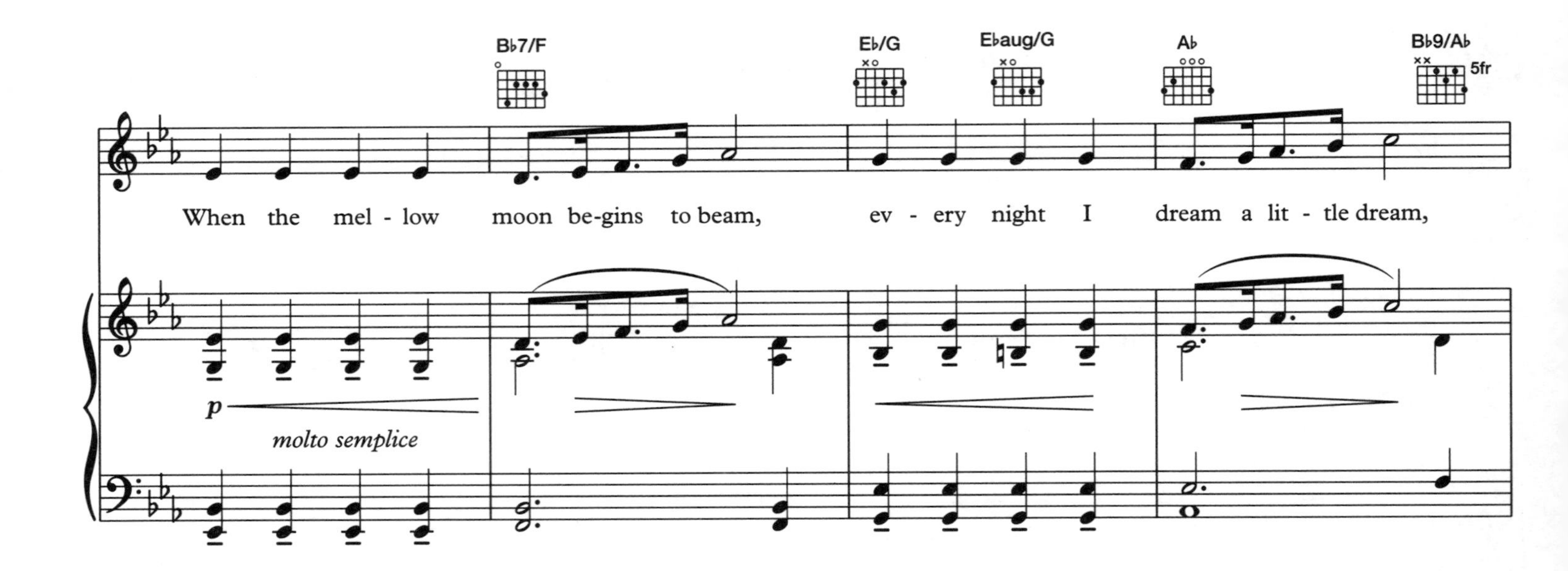

E♭
B♭7/F
Gm
Cm
Cdim7
-though I re - al - ize as well as you, it is sel - dom that a dream comes true,
B♭/F
F7♭9
B♭/F
B♭dim7/F
Fm7/C
B♭7
poco rall.
to me it's clear that he'll ap - pear.
poco rall.
dim.
slowly
E♭
E♭m
B♭m/D♭
Some-day he'll come a-long, the man I love, and he'll be big and strong,
slowly
p molto semplice e dolce
C7
Fm7♭5
B♭7
E♭
A♭maj7
the man I love, and when he comes my way, I'll do my best to make him

Gm
B♭13sus4
B♭13
E♭
E♭m
stay.
He'll look at me and smile,
I'll un - der-stand,
p
B♭m/D♭
C7
Fm7♭5
and in a lit - tle while,
he'll take my hand,
and though it seems ab-surd,
B♭7
Fm7
B♭13
E♭
A♭
E♭
Adim7
A♭7
G7
I know we both won't say a word.
Cm
Cm7
D7/C
Ddim7/C
Cm
May - be I shall meet him Sun - day, may - be Mon - day, may - be
mp
poco espr.

G7
Cm
Cm7
D7/C
Ddim7/C
poco rit.
Cm
C7♭9/G
not, still I'm sure to meet him one day, may - be Tues - day will be
poco rit.
dim.
A♭
B♭7
a tempo
E♭
E♭m
my good news day. He'll build a lit - tle home, just meant for two,
a tempo
p
B♭m/D♭
C7
Fm7♭5
from which I'll ne - ver roam, who would, would you? And so all else a-bove,
B♭7
Fm7
B♭13
E♭
A♭
1.
E♭
B♭9/A♭
Gdim7
G♭dim7
Fdim7
2.
E♭
5fr
4fr
I'm wait-ing for the man I love. love.
8va

MOONLIGHT AND ROSES

Words by BEN BLACK and CHARLES DANIELS
Music adapted from Andatino in Db by EDWIN LEMARE

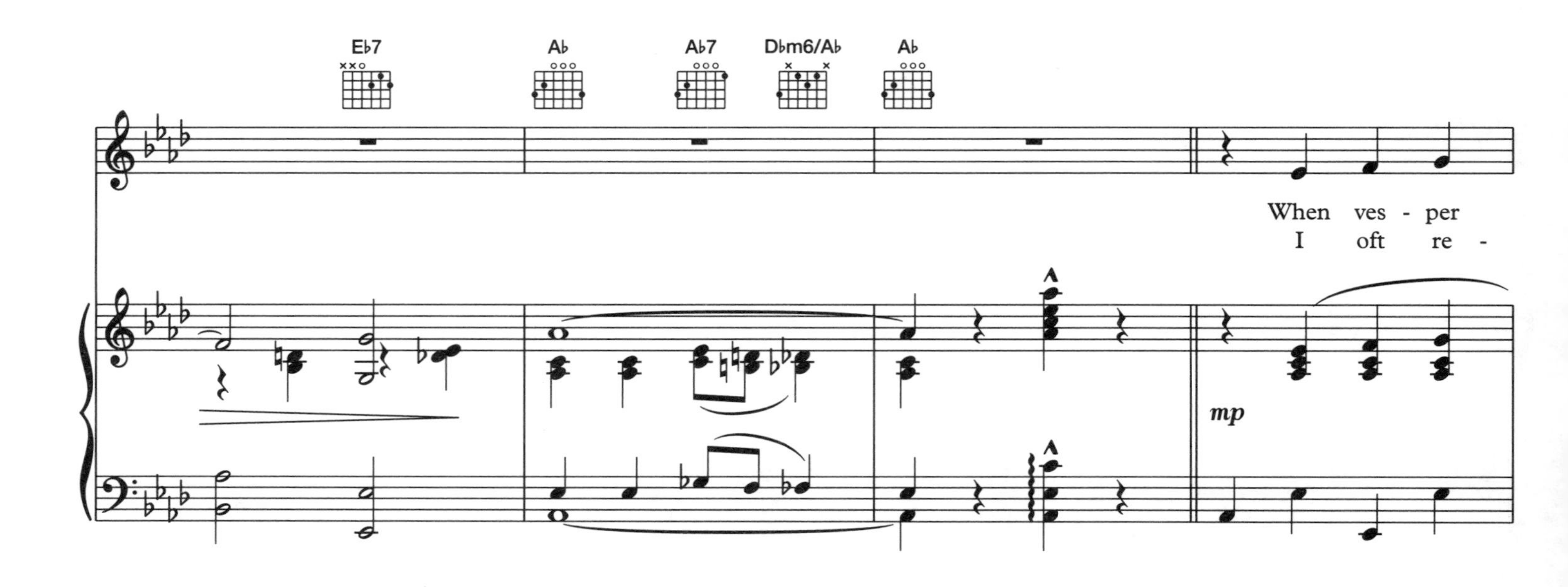

A♭
E♭
fall.
'Tis then my heart grows fon - der as through the
dreams,
and then a - las, we part - ed, you left me
Fm7
B♭13
B♭7
E♭7
B♭m7
E♭aug
flowers I wan - der with thoughts so true dear, al - ways of you, dear.
brok - en heart - ed, but still I yearn, dear, for your re - turn, dear.
A♭
D♭/A♭
A♭
E♭7/A♭
3fr
A♭
Moon - light and ro - ses bring won - der - ful
Moon - light and ro - ses bring won - der - ful

Eb7
memories of you, my heart re-
memories of you, my heart re-
Eb11
Eb7
Bbm7
Ebaug
Ab
-pos - es in beau - ti - ful thoughts so true,
-pos - es in beau - ti - ful thoughts so true,
Db/Ab
Ab
Eb7/Ab
3fr
Ab
June light dis - clos - es love's
June light dis - clos - es love's

D♭6
old - en dreams spark - ling a - new.
Moon -
old - en dreams spark - ling a - new.
Moon -
mf - f
A♭
D♭/A♭
F7
B♭7
E♭7
- light and ros - es bring mem - ories of
- light and ros - es bring mem - ories of
1.
2.
A♭
E♭7
E♭aug
A♭
A♭7
D♭m6/A♭
A♭
D.C.
you.
you.
you.
you.

MOUNTAIN GREENERY

Words by LORENZ HART
Music by RICHARD RODGERS

G Gaug C6/G F/G D7/G G7
Now's the time to trust to your wan - der - lust,
Cof - fee's just as grand with a lit - tle sand,
poco a poco cresc.
E7 Am G/D G11 G7
poco rit.
in the ci - ty's dust you wait, must you wait? Just you wait:
eat and you'll grow fat - ter boy. 'S'mat - ter boy? 'At - ta boy!
poco rit.
a tempo
C Am Dm7 G7 C Am Dm7 G7
In a moun - tain green - er - y, where God paints the sce - ne - ry,
a tempo
p-f
C F D7 G Am7 A♯dim7 G/B
just two cra - zy peo - ple to - ge - ther.

C Am Dm7 G7 C Am Dm7 G7
While you love your lov - er, let blue skies be your cov - er-let,
How we love se - quest - er - ing where no pests are pes - ter-ing,
mp
C F D7 G Am7 A#dim7
when it rains, we'll laugh at the wea - ther,
no dear ma - ma holds us in te - ther!
cresc.
G C7#5 F6 C7
and if you're good, I'll search for wood,
Mos - qui - tos here won't bite you, dear,
F6 Fm6 Em7
so you can cook
I'll let them sting

D7 G11 G7 C Am
— while I stand look - - ing. Beans could
— me on the fin - - ger. We could
mp
Dm7 G7 C Am Dm7 G7 C Am
get no keen - er re - cep - tion in a bea - ne - ry, bless our
find no clean - er re - treat from life's ma - chi - ne - ry, than our
Dm7 G7
1. C G11 G7
moun - tain green - er - y home!
moun - tain green - er - y
2. C
Fine
3. Trio-Patter
C
home!
home!
mf
p
fp

G7/B
C
He: When the world was young, old Fa - ther A - dam with sin would grap - ple, so we're en -
p
G7
C
- ti - tled to just one ap - ple, I mean to make ap - ple sauce.
(over L.H.)
mf
G7/B
C
She: Un - der-neath the bough, we'll learn a les - son from Mis - ter O - mar, be-neath the
p
stacc.
G7
C
eyes of no Pa and no Ma, old la - dy na - ture is boss.
(over L.H.)
mf

Em A7 Am Em B7
He: Wash-ing dish - es, catch - ing fish - es in the run - ning stream, we'll
mp giocoso
Em A7 D11 D7 G7
curse the smell a' ci - tro-nel - la, e - ven when we dream.
mf
C G7/B C
She: Head up-on the ground, your dow - ny pil - low is just a boul - der. He: I'll have new
mp
stacc.
G7/B C C9♯5
dim - ples be - fore I'm old - er, but life is peach - es and cream, and if you're good,
f

F
C7
F
Fm6
I'll search for wood,
so you can cook
Em
D7
G11
G7
while I stand look - - ing.
C
Am
Dm7
G7
C
Am
Dm7
G7
Beans could get no keen - er re - cep - tion in a bea - ne - ry,
mp
C
Am
Dm7
G7
C
bless our moun - tain green - er - y home!
mf
p

MY YIDDISHE MOMME

Words by JACK YELLEN
Music by JACK YELLEN and LEW POLLACK

rit.
B♭m
3fr
F7
B♭m
E♭dim7/B♭
B♭m
E♭dim7/B♭
B♭m
F7
D7
east side te - ne - ment, three flights up in the rear to where my child-hood days were spent. It
haunt my me-mo - ry, each plain-tive note, each ten-der word a mo - ther's prayer for me. What
rit.
Gm
Cdim7/G
Gm
Cdim7/G
Gm
Cdim7/G
Gm
Cm
was - n't much like pa - ra - dise, but 'mid the dirt and all, there sat the sweet - est
have I that I would not give to cross the trails of time, back to those child-hood
rit.
ff
Gm
rall.
A7
E♭7
D7
Gm
an - gel, one that I fond - ly call. My Yid - di - she
by - gones, back to you, mom - me mine? A Yid - di - she
rall.
pp

Gm
D7
mom - me, I need her more than ev - er now, my Yid-di-she
mom - me, sie macht noch sütz die gan-zer velt, a Yid-di-she
p–mf
Gm
mom - me, I'd love to kiss that wrink-led brow.
mom - me, oiy vey vie bit - ter ven sie k'velt.
D7/A
Gm/B♭
Cm
Am7♭5
D7
Gm
I long to hold her hands once more as in days gone by,
Ich darf doch dan - kin Gott vüss ehr hodt eer noch ba - sharecht,

D7/F♯
Gm
Adim7
D7♭9
Adim7
D7
Gm
and ask her to for - give me for things I did that made her cry.
ere vaist nit vie trau - rig sie vecht ven sie geht a - veck su gich.
D7
How few were her plea - sures, she ne - ver cared for fash - ion's styles,
In vass - er und fi - er vult sie gel - off - en fur eer kint,
Gm
her jew - els and trea - sures, she found them in her ba - by's smiles.
nischt hal - ten eer ty - er, duss iss gev - iss die gres - ter süade.

Cm/G G7 Cm Gm Cm A♭7/C Cm
— Oh, I know that I owe what I am to - day, to that
— Oiy, vie glück - lich und reich iss dair mensch vüss hadt, az a
Gm Cdim7/G Gm E♭7/G Gm Cm Gm Cm
rall.
dear lit - tle la - dy so old and grey, to that won - der - ful Yid - di - she mom - me
schein - er Ma - don - na ge - schenkt fon Gott. Nür a ol - titch - ker Yid - di - she Mom - me,
ff
1. 2.
D7 Gm Gm D7 Gm
D.C.
of mine. My Yid - di - she of mine.
momme mine. A Yid - di - she momme mine.
sfz

NOBODY'S SWEETHEART

Words by GUS KAHN and BILLY MEYERS
Music by ERNEST ERDMAN and ELMER SCHOEBEL

Am7♭5/G
Em
Gm/B♭
D/A
A7/G
D6/F♯
— and in our home town each boy a - round
— as you went your way at close of day,
Em
A
D7/F♯
A7
longed to be your beau, but things are
past the old red mill. You're dressed in
D
B
B7
Em
A7
dif - ferent to - day, I'm migh - ty sor - ry to
sa - tins to - day, but still your eyes seem to
D7
G
Dm/F
E7
say: You're no - bo - dy's sweet - heart now,
say:
mp–f

A7
they don't ba - by you some - how,
D7
Em
E7
A7
fan - cy hose silk - en gown, you'd be out of place
D
Edim7
D7
G
Dm/F
in your own home town. When you walk down the a - ven -
E7
A7
- ue, I just can't be - lieve that it's you.

E♭dim7
G7/D
C
Cm
3fr
Paint - ed lips,
paint - ed eyes,
G
E7
A7
D7
G
wear - ing a bird of pa - ra - dise,
it all seems
Bm/F♯
Dm/F
E7
Am7
Am7♭5
G
A9/E
D7/F♯
wrong some - how,
that you're no - bo - dy's sweet - heart
1.
G
B♭dim7
D7
now.
You're
2.
G
Am7
Am7♭5
D
G
now.
D.𝄋
fz

ON MOTHER KELLY'S DOORSTEP

Words and Music by GEORGE A STEVENS

B♭
Fm7
B♭
A♭/E♭
E♭
al - ley. On Mo-ther Kel-ly's door - step, I'm won-der-ing now,
F♯dim7
B♭
E♭
A♭m
3fr
E♭
Fm7
B♭7
if li'l gal Nel - ly re-mem-bers Joe, her beau, and does she
Cm
D7/A
E♭/B♭
Fm7
B♭7
love me like she used to, on Mo-ther Kel-ly's door - step,
1.
E♭
A♭
B♭7
2.
E♭
F♯dim7
E♭
down Pa-ra-dise Row? On Mo-ther Kel-ly's
f

ONLY A ROSE

Words by BRIAN HOOKER
Music by RUDOLPH FRIML

Fbaug
Ab/Eb
Fm7
Bbm7
poco rit
Eb11
Eb7
tell the love I love best, 'Love is a rose'.
poco rit.
legato
Ab
Db
On-ly a rose I give you, on-ly a song
legato
Ab
Eb
rit.
dy-ing a - way, on-ly a smile to keep in
rit.
L.H.
Ab
C
G7
me-mo-ry, un-til we meet an-oth-er

rit.
a tempo
C
F7
Bb13
Eb7
Ab
day.
On-ly a rose
to
whis - per,
p
Db
blush-ing as ro - - ses do,
cresc.
Bbm
Bbm7b5
Ab/Eb
'I'll bring a-long a smile or a song for a - ny - one',
f
a tempo
1.
poco rit.
2.
rit. molto
on-ly a rose for you.
you.
pp

PASADENA

Words by GRANT CLARKE and EDGAR LESLIE
Music by HARRY WARREN

G/D D7 G B♭7 E♭7
for my des - ti - na - - tion far
I'll be strik - ing po - - ses with
rit.
D7 G7 Gdim7 G7 D7 G7 C
be - yond the west - ern plain. To see my;
my lov - ing all in all, be - side my;
Home in Pa - sa -
mf
Em C7 F A7
- de - na, home, where grass is green - er,
Dm Dm7♭5 C/G C7 B7
where hon - ey bees hum me - lo - dies, and o - range

E G7 D7/A G7/B C Em
4fr
trees scent the breeze. I'm gon-na be a home sweet hom-
C7 F E
-er, there I'll set-tle down be-neath the
Dm/F B7 Cmaj7/G B7/F♯ B♭7/F A7 D7 D7♭5/A♭
palms, in some-one's arms in Pa-sa-de-
f
G7 C C7/B♭ F6/A A♭7 C/G D7 G7 C G7 C
1. 2.
-na town. town.
D.𝄋

S-H-I-N-E

Words by CECIL MACK and LEW BROWN
Music by FORD T DABNEY

B♭7
E♭
G♭dim7
worked like sin, had a grin guar - an - teed to bring the
smil - ing face, same old place, be - in' broke to him was
B♭7
E♭
Cm
bus - iness in. Ev - ery day, when they'd ask him how he
no dis - grace. What a mob, hang - in' round to watch him
p
F7
B♭/F
D7♭5/A♭
G7
Fm6/C
G7/B
got that way, he would tell 'em, 'If you en - vy me, just
on the job, stand - in' on the cor - ner all day long, they'd
Cm
F7
B♭7
E♭/G
E♭m/G♭
E♭dim7/G♭
try my re - ci - pe'. 'Cause my hair is
lis - ten to his song. Shine a - way your
p-f

Fm7 B♭7 E♭/G E♭m/G♭ E♭dim7/G♭
cur - ly, 'cause my teeth are
blues - ies, shine, start with your
Fm7 B♭7 G7/B Dm/A 4fr G7
pear - ly, just be - cause I
shoes - ies. Shine each place up,
Cm G7/B Cm G7/D Cm/E♭ F7/A Cm/G F7
al - ways wear a smile, like to dress up
make it look like new, shine your face up,
B♭7/D A♭/C B♭7 A♭/C B♭7/D E♭/G E♭m/G♭ E♭dim7/G♭
in the la - test style, 'cause I'm glad I'm
wear a smile or two. Shine your these and

Fm7 Bb7 G7
liv - ing, take trou - ble smil - ing, and the
thos - ies, you'll find that ev - ery - thing will
Cm G7/B Cm Fm
world is mine. I'm a luc - ky fel - la,
turn out fine, folks will shine up to ya,
Eb C7 Fm/Ab C7/G Fm Bb11 3fr Bb7#5
got the sun for my um - brel - la, that's why they call me
ev - ery-one will how - dy do ya, you'll make the whole world
1. Eb Bb7 Ab/C Bb7b9/D
'Shine'.
2. Eb Eb7/Db Fm/C Cb7 Eb/Bb Bb7#5 Eb
shine!
D.S.
f
sfz

SOMETIMES I'M HAPPY

Words by IRVING CAESAR and CLIFFORD GREY
Music by VINCENT YOUMANS

C7
Caug
F
F7
are not near.
in the skies.
Bb
Adim7
Bb
Bbm6
She: All that you claim must be true, for I'm just the same as
He: Tell me that you will be true! She: That will all de - pend on
mf
G7
rall.
C7
you.
you, dear!
rall.
F
C7
F
C7
Both: Some - times I'm hap - py, some - times I'm blue,
p - mf

F
C7
F
C7
my dis - po - si - tion
de - pends on you,
F
Am7♭5
Adim7
B♭
Gdim7
B♭/F
B♭m6
F
I ne - ver mind the rain from the skies,
if I can
Cm/E♭
D7
Gm
C7
F
C7
find the sun in your eyes.
Some - times I love you,
F
C7
F
C7
some - times I hate you,
but when I hate you,

F
C7
F
Am7♭5
Adim7
it's 'cause I love you.
That's how I am, so
B♭
Gdim7
B♭/F
B♭m6
F/C
C11
C13
what can I do?
I'm hap - py when I'm with
1.
F
F/A
A♭dim7
Gm7
C7
you!
2.
F
Fdim7
F
D.C.
you!

STRIKE UP THE BAND

Music and Lyrics by
GEORGE GERSWHIN and IRA GERSHWIN

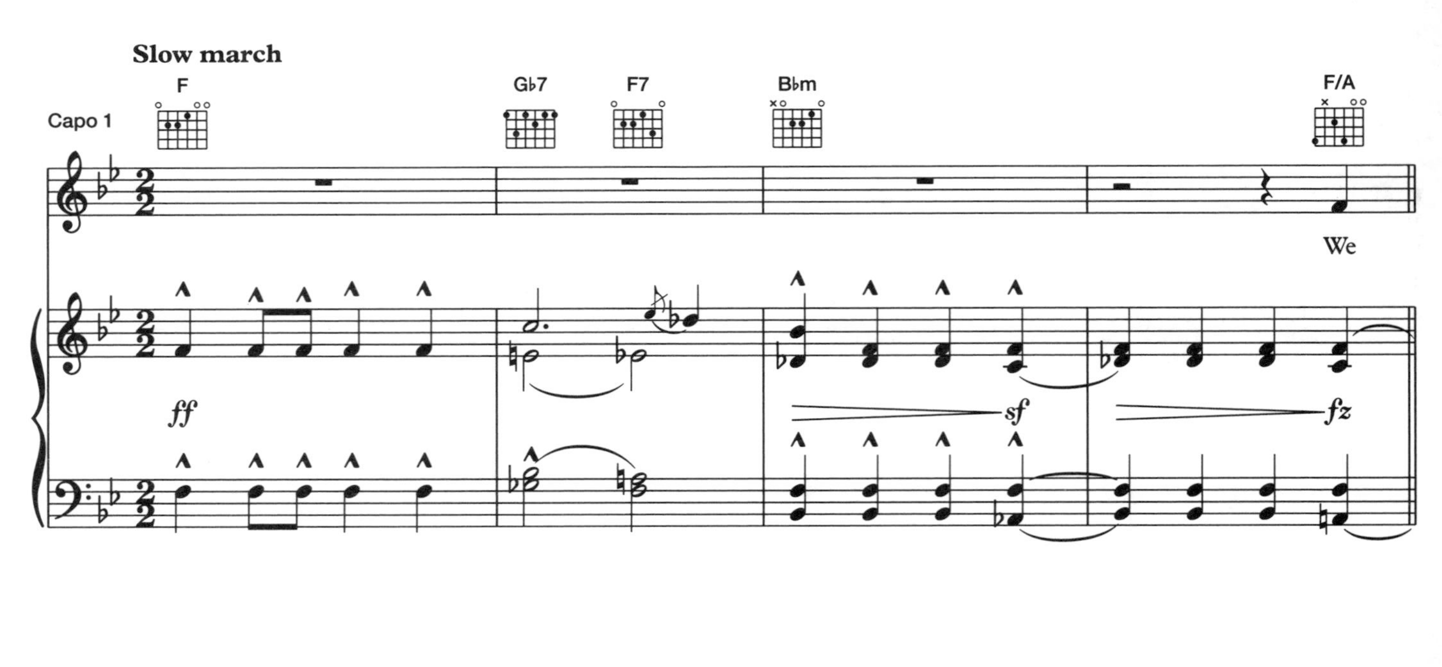

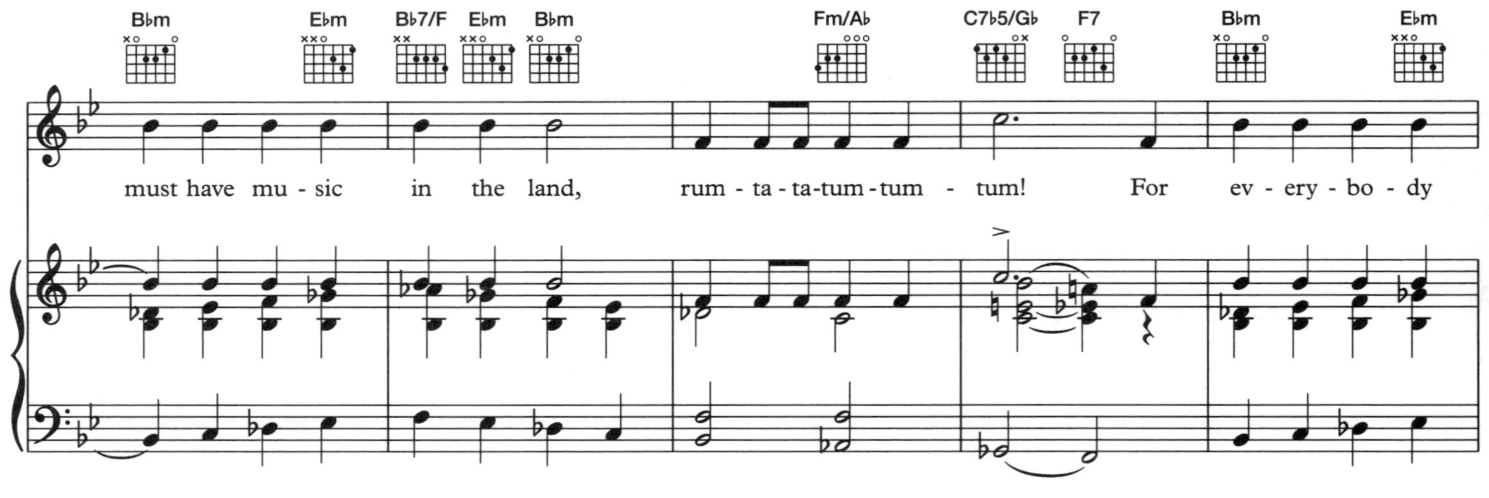

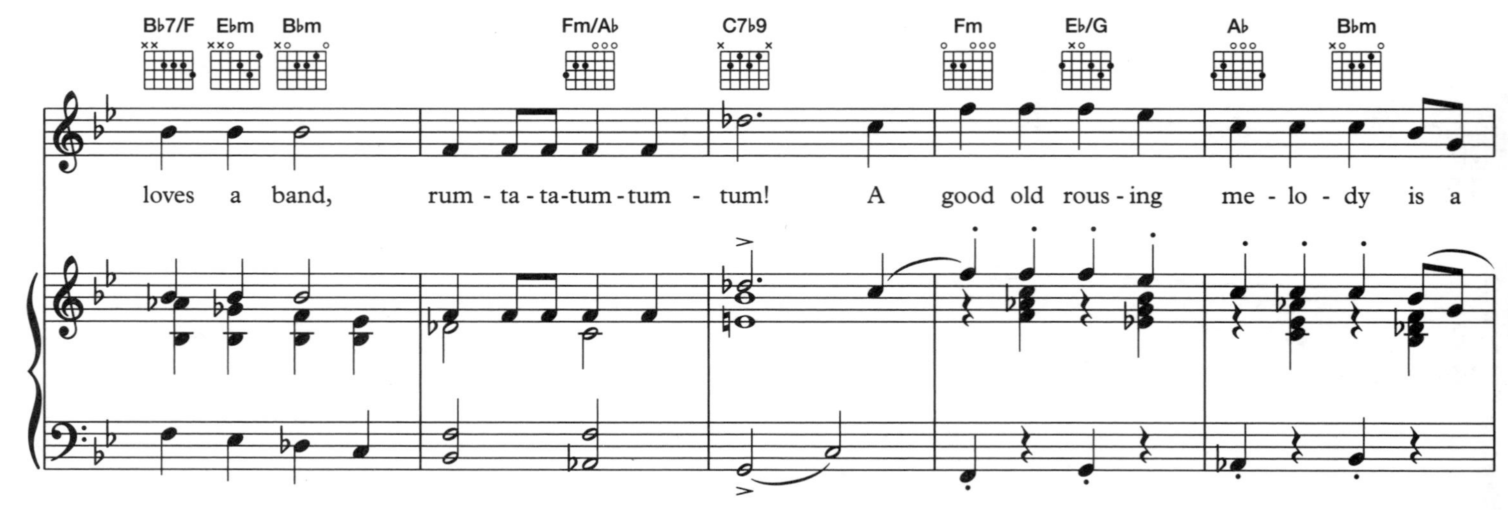

Fm/C
C7
Fm
C7/G
F
C7
F/A
B♭
joy and in - spi - ra - tion, a hun - dred mil - lion folks a - gree that a
F
C7
F
F7
B♭m
E♭m
B♭7/F
E♭m
B♭m
tune can stir a na - tion, so, mu - sic mas - ter, take com - mand,
molto marcato
Fm/A♭
C7♭5/G♭
F7
rall.
B♭m
E♭9
3fr
rum - ta - ta - tum - tum - tum! Our hearts will beat to beat the band,
rall.
B♭m
Fm/A♭
G♭maj7
F
rum - ta - ta - tum - tum, rum - ta - ta - tum - tum, rum - ta - ta - tum - tum - tum! Let the

B♭
Bdim7
drums roll out, let the trum - pet call, while the
(spoken) Boom boom boom! (imitation of Trumpet) Ta-ta - ra - ta - ta - ta - ta!
mf–f
F7
B♭
B♭11
3fr
B♭7
peo - ple shout, 'Strike up the band!' Hear the
(shouted) Hoo - ray!
E♭
Edim7
cym - bals ring, call - ing one and all to that
(spoken) Tszing-Tszing-tszing! (Trumpet) Ta - ta - ra - ta - ta - ta - ta!
B♭7
E♭
Cm7♭5
hap - py swing, strike up the band! Yan - kee
mar - tial And we'll
(shouted) Left, right!

B♭ Gm B♭ E♭/G Am D7 Am D7
doo doodle-oo, doodle - oo, we'll come through doodle-oo, doodle - oo, for the
all give a cheer, as we stand to the man with the stick in his hand. He's the
Gm C7 Gm C7 F7 B♭
red white and blue, doodle - oo lend a hand! With the flag unfurled,
man who's command of the band, makes the band, and you can't go wrong
Dm7 G7 Cm7 Gm/D E♭ Em7♭5 F7sus4 F13
we can face the world.
with a happy song.
Hey leader, strike up the
1. 2.
B♭ G C F7 B♭
band! Let the band!
sf f

THAT OLD FASHIONED MOTHER OF MINE

Words by WORTON DAVID
Music by HORATIO NICHOLLS

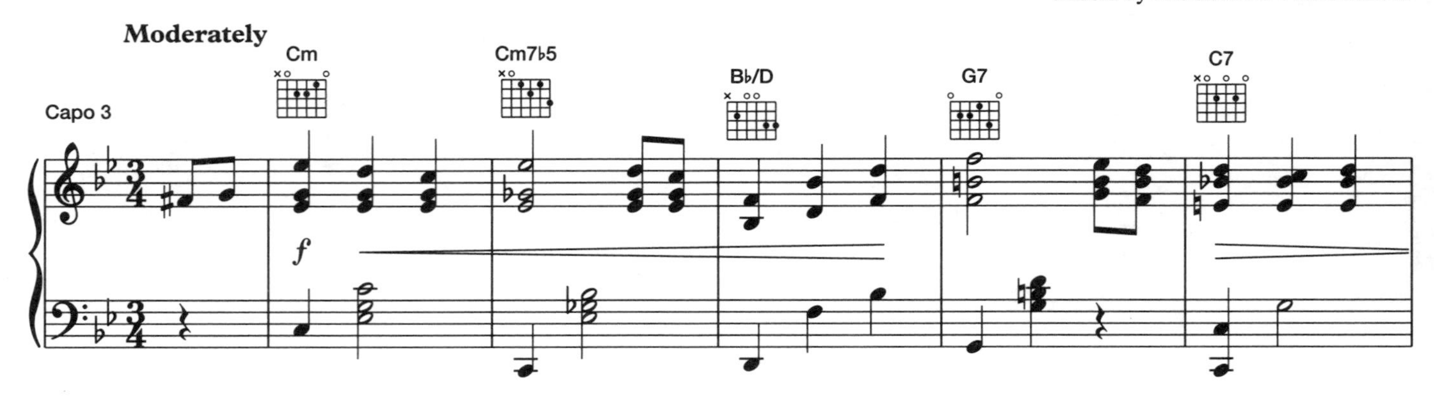

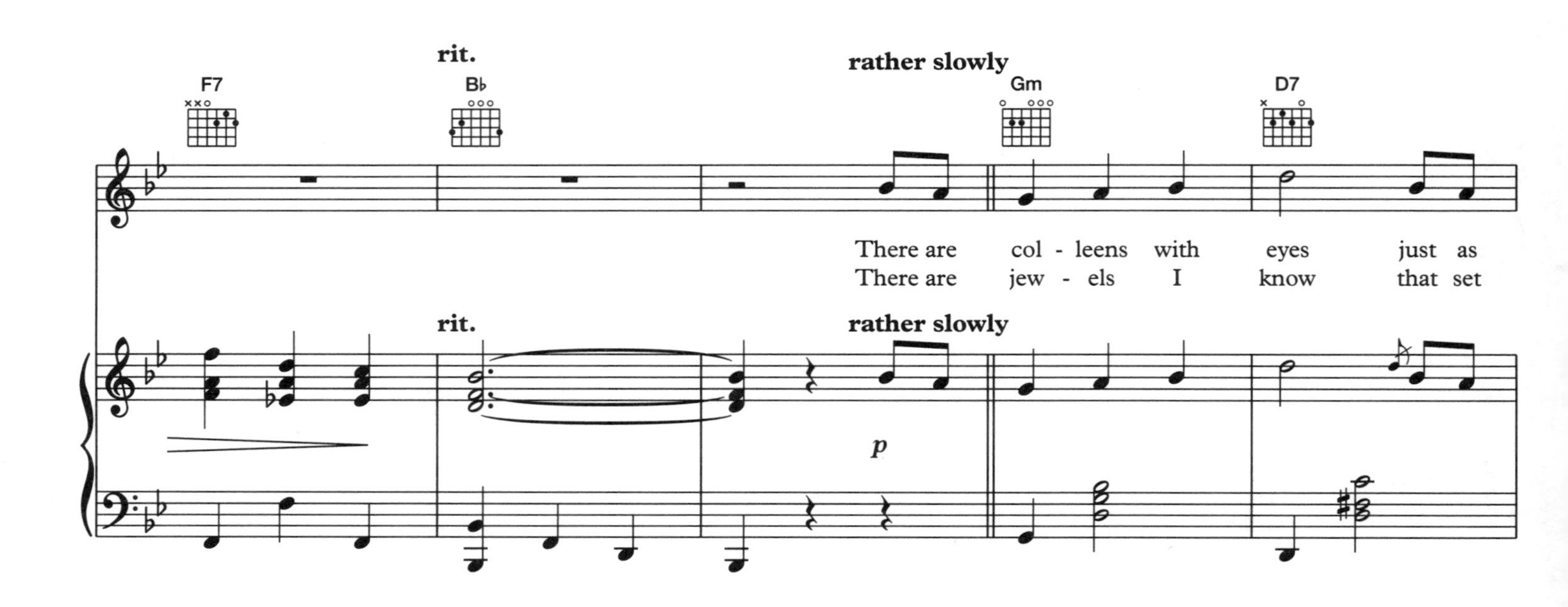

D7
Gm
G
hand - some and wise, but deep in my heart, there's a
they wor - ship so, but there is a jew - el that
G7
Cm
C7
sweet me - mo - ry of some - one who still holds at -
I wor - ship more, it's set in the heart of the
ten.
rall.
F7
tenderly
B♭
- trac - tions for me.
one I a - dore.
Just an old fa - shioned la - dy with
rall.
tenderly
p
E♭
E♭m
3fr
B♭
F7
old fa - shioned ways, and a smile that says wel - come to

B♭
B♭7
E♭
G♭7
you, __ an old fa - shioned bed - side where
B♭/F
Gdim7
B♭/F
Gm
C7
she kneels and prays, when the toil of the long day is
rit.
a tempo
F7sus4
F7
B♭
through. __ Though she wears no fine clothes or no
rit.
a tempo
ten.
E♭
E♭m
3fr
B♭
B♭7
rich silk - en hose, still there's some - thing that makes her di -

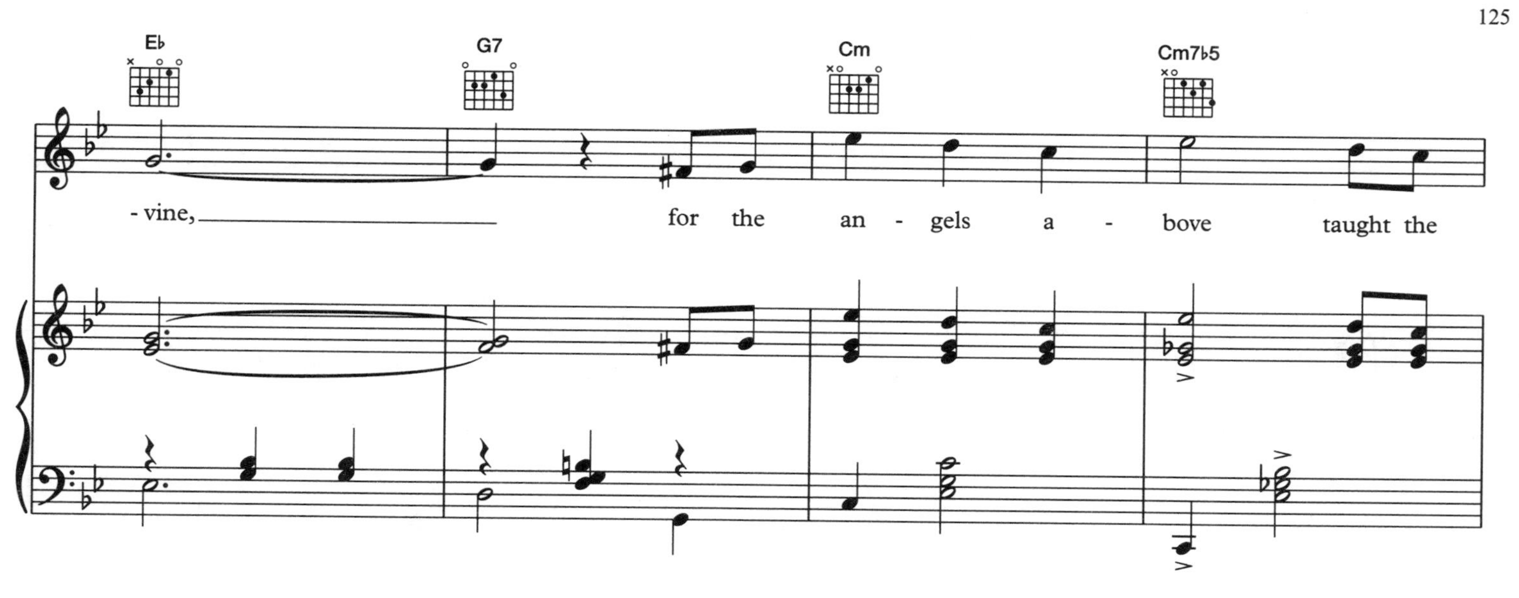
E♭
G7
Cm
Cm7♭5
-vine, for the an - gels a - bove taught the

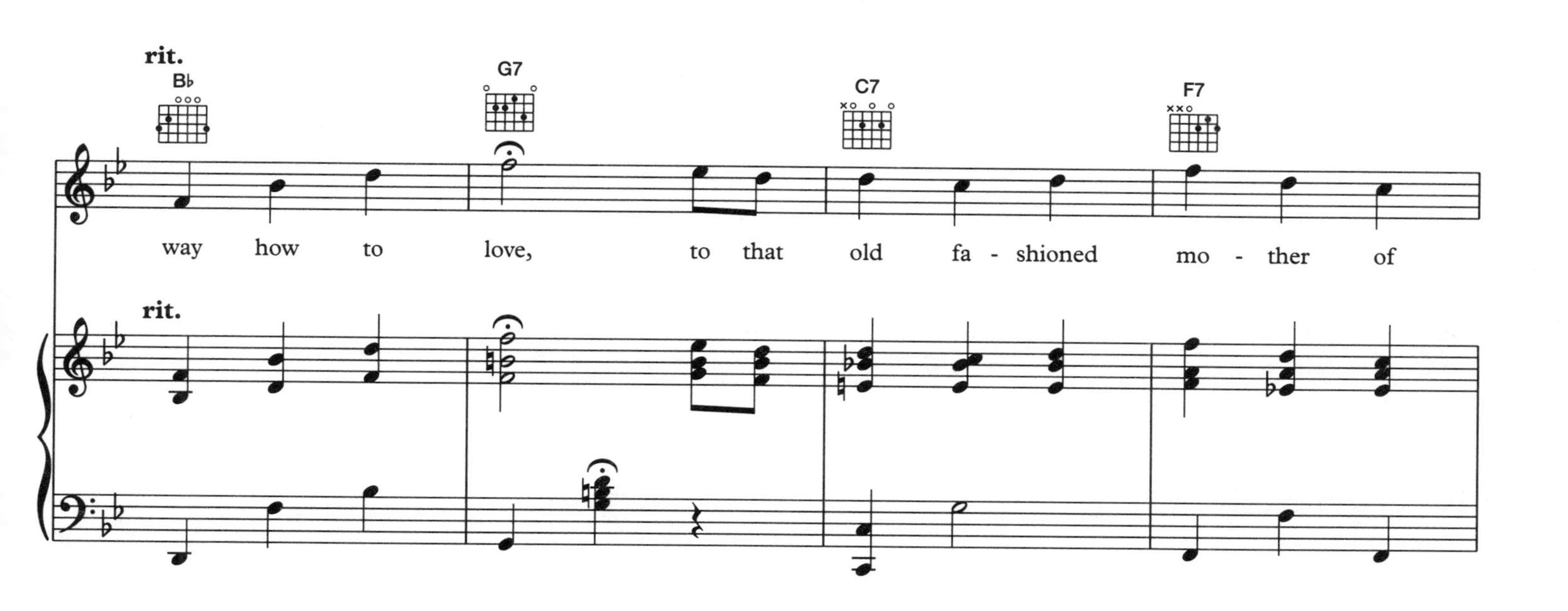
rit.
B♭
G7
C7
F7
way how to love, to that old fa - shioned mo - ther of
rit.

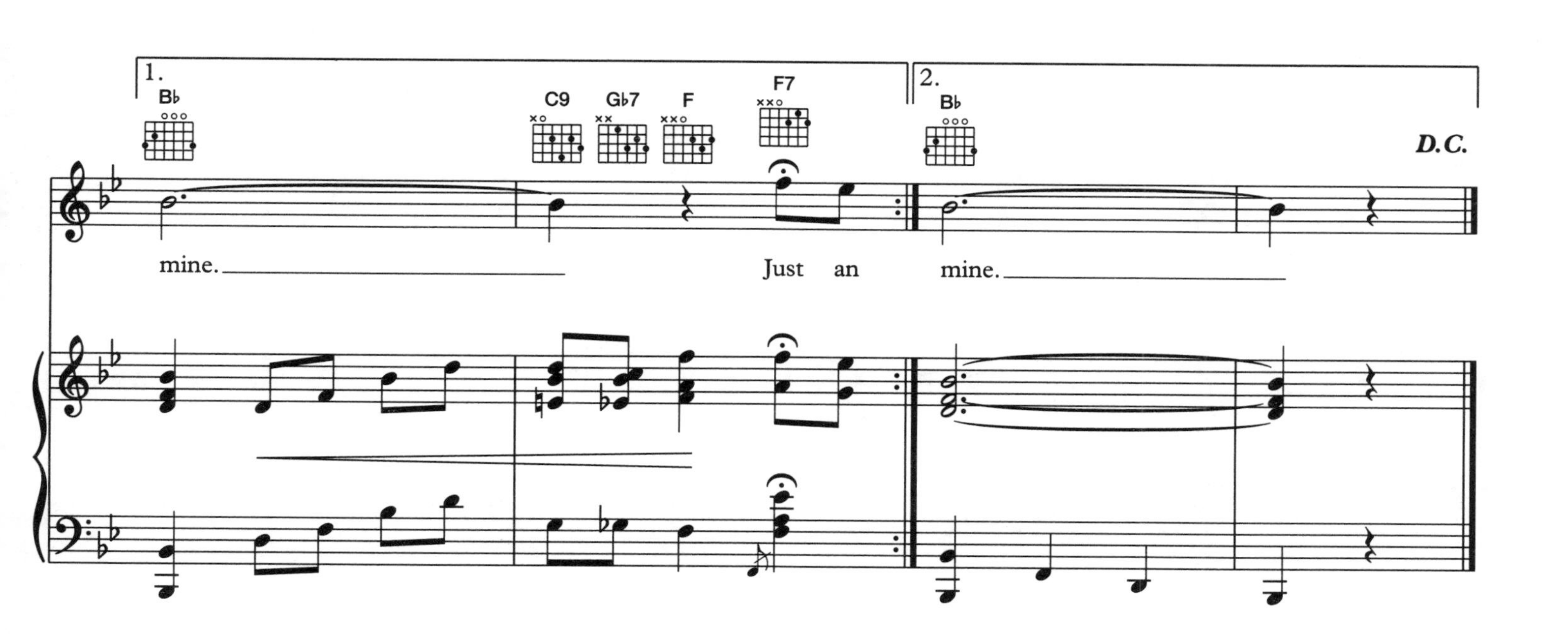
1.
B♭
C9
G♭7
F
F7
2.
B♭
D.C.
mine. Just an mine.

THERE'S A BLUE RIDGE ROUND MY HEART VIRGINIA

Words by ALFRED BRYAN
Music by FRED PHILLIPS and IRA SCHUSTER

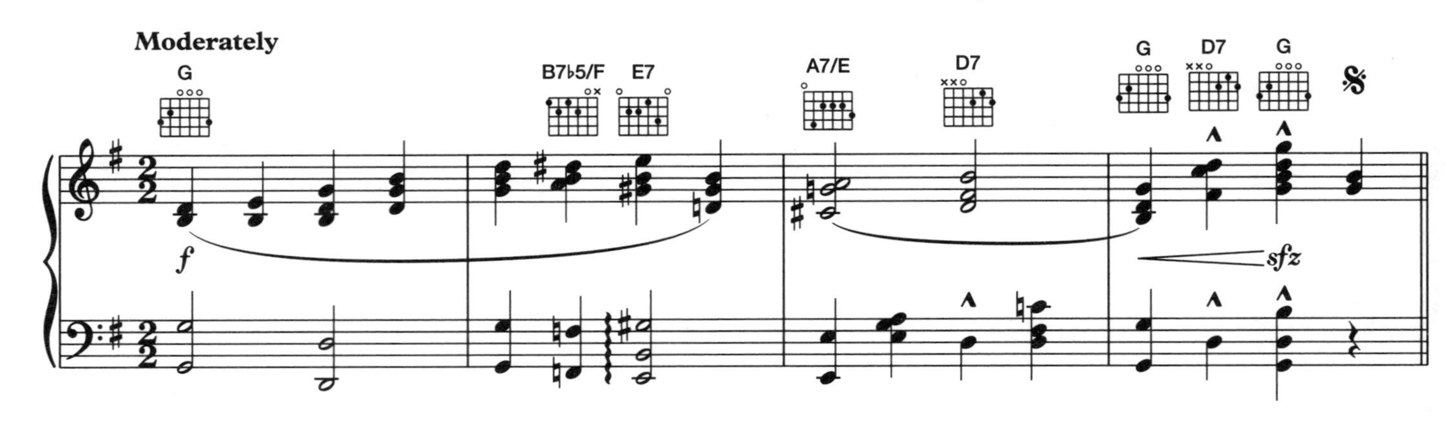

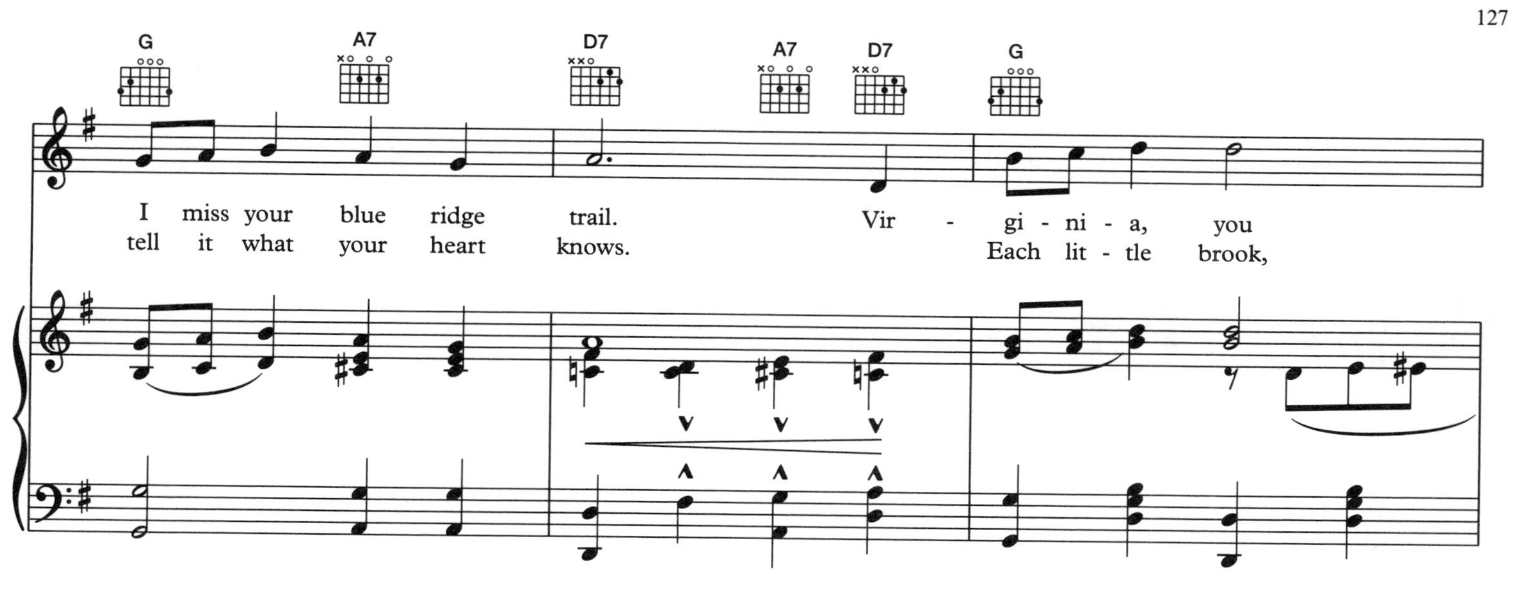
G
A7
D7
A7
D7
G
I miss your blue ridge trail. Vir - gi - ni - a, you
tell it what your heart knows. Each lit - tle brook,

D7
G
Gdim7
G6
A7
keep call - ing too, o - ver the hill and dale, I've been lone - some
each sha - dy nook, tell 'em no more I'll roam, tell them I am

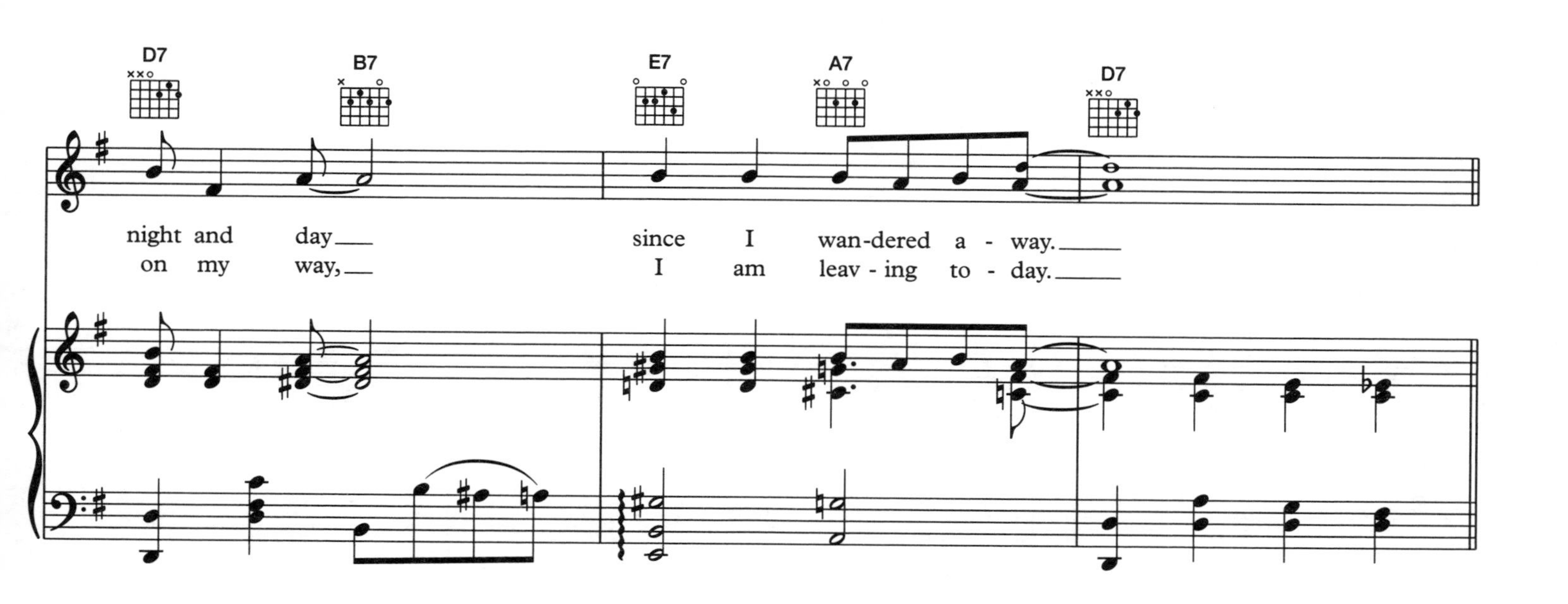
D7
B7
E7
A7
D7
night and day since I wan - dered a - way.
on my way, I am leav - ing to - day.

G
Gdim7
G
A7
There's a blue ridge round my heart, Vir - gin - - ia,
p–f
D7
G6
I'm as lone - some as the lone - some pine.
Say,
B7
Em
B7
Em
I would give my soul if I could but stroll
A7
D7
where the flo - wers nod to you,
and the birds sing, 'How d'you do?'

G
Gdim7
G
A7
D7
In that blue ridge round my heart, Vir - gin - - ia, rings a song and
B
E7
all day long I pine to see the time when your sun - shine
A7
F#7
G
fills the sky, all my cares will say good - bye, for there's a blue ridge
B7♭5/F
E7
A7
D7
1.
G
D7
2.
G
D7
G
D.𝄋
round my heart, Vir - gin - ia mine. mine.
sfz

THOU SWELL

Words by LORENZ HART
Music by RICHARD RODGERS

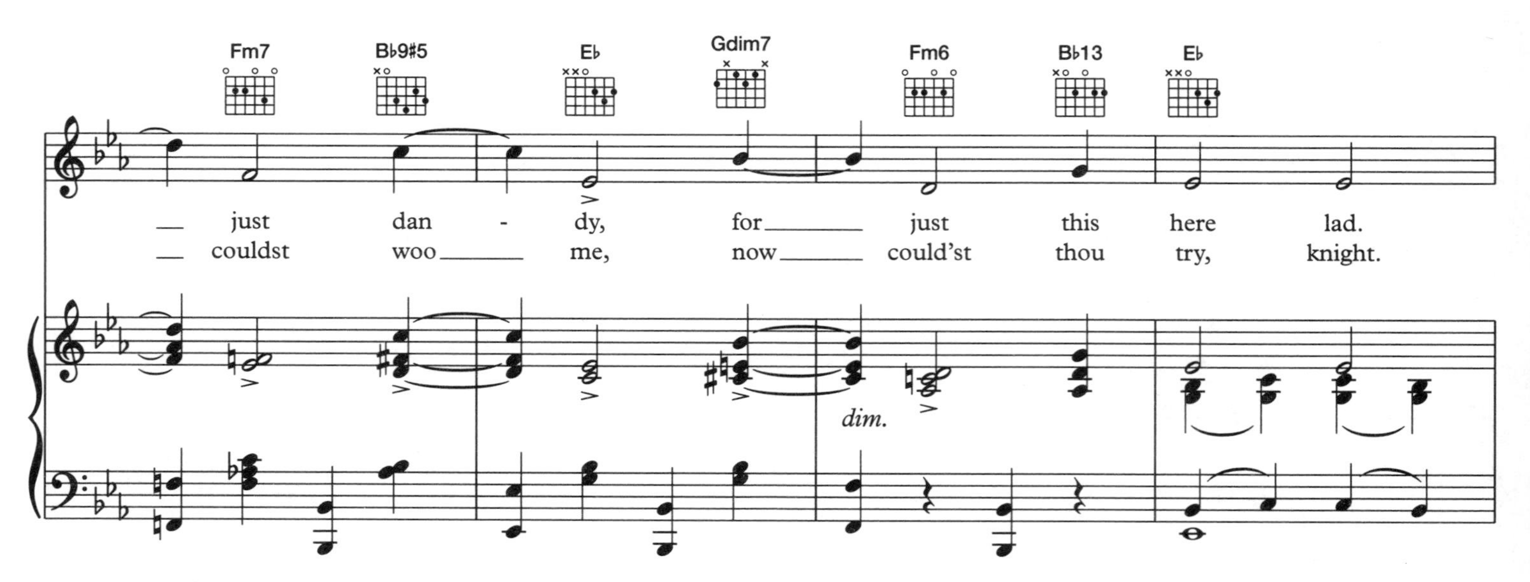

B♭7 E♭ Fm B♭7 E♭ D7
You're such a fist - ful, my eyes are mist - ful, are you too wist - ful to care? Do
I'd mur-mur 'Swell' too, and like it well too. More thou wilt tell to San - dy, thou
Fm7 B♭9♯5 E♭ Gdim7 Fm6 B♭13 E♭
say you care to say, 'Come near, lad'.
art dan - dy, now art thou my knight.
dim.
scherzando
Gm Cm D7 Gm E♭ Cm D7 Gm
You are so grace - ful, have you wings? You have a face full of nice things.
Thine arms are mar - tial, thou hast grace, my cheek is par - tial to thy face,
scherzando
Cm F7 B♭6 Gm Cm F11 F7 B♭7 F9
rall. rit.
You have no speak - ing voice, dear, with ev - ery word it sings.
and if thy lips grow wea - ry, mine are their rest - ing place.
Thou
rall. rit.

slowly with grace
Bb7 F9 Bb7 F9 Bb7 F9 Bb7 Bb9
swell, thou wit - ty, thou sweet, thou grand! Wouldst
slowly with grace
mf
Eb6 Bb9 Eb6 Bb9 Eb6 Bb9 Eb/G Gbdim7
kiss me pret - ty? Wouldst hold my hand? Both thine eyes
mf
Bb7/F C7/E Fm Bb7/D Eb Ebaug/G
are cute too, what they do to me. Hear me
dim.
mp
Ab G7 Cm F7 Bb7 Bb6 Bb9#5/Ab Ab6 F9 Bb7 F9
hol-ler, I choose a sweet lol-lo - pa-loo-sa in thee. I'd feel so
mf
p

Bb7 F9 Bb7 F9 Bb7 Bb9 Eb6 Bb9
rich in a hut for two, two rooms and
Eb6 Bb9 Eb6 Bb9 Eb/G Gbdim7 Bb7/F C7/E
kit - chen, I'm sure would do, give me just a plot of,
mf
Fm Bb7/D G7 Caug C7 F7 Bb7
not a lot of land, and thou swell, thou wit - ty, thou
1. Eb F#dim7 Bb7/F F9
grand! Thou
mf
2. Eb Bb9/Ab Eb/G Bb7/F Eb
grand!
D.C.
mf
sf

WAY DOWN YONDER IN NEW ORLEANS

Words and Music by
HENRY CREAMER and TURNER LAYTON

Em
B7
Em
Guess! Where do you think I'm go - ing when the nights start grow-ing long? I
Guess! What do you think I'm think - ing when I'm think - ing all night long? I

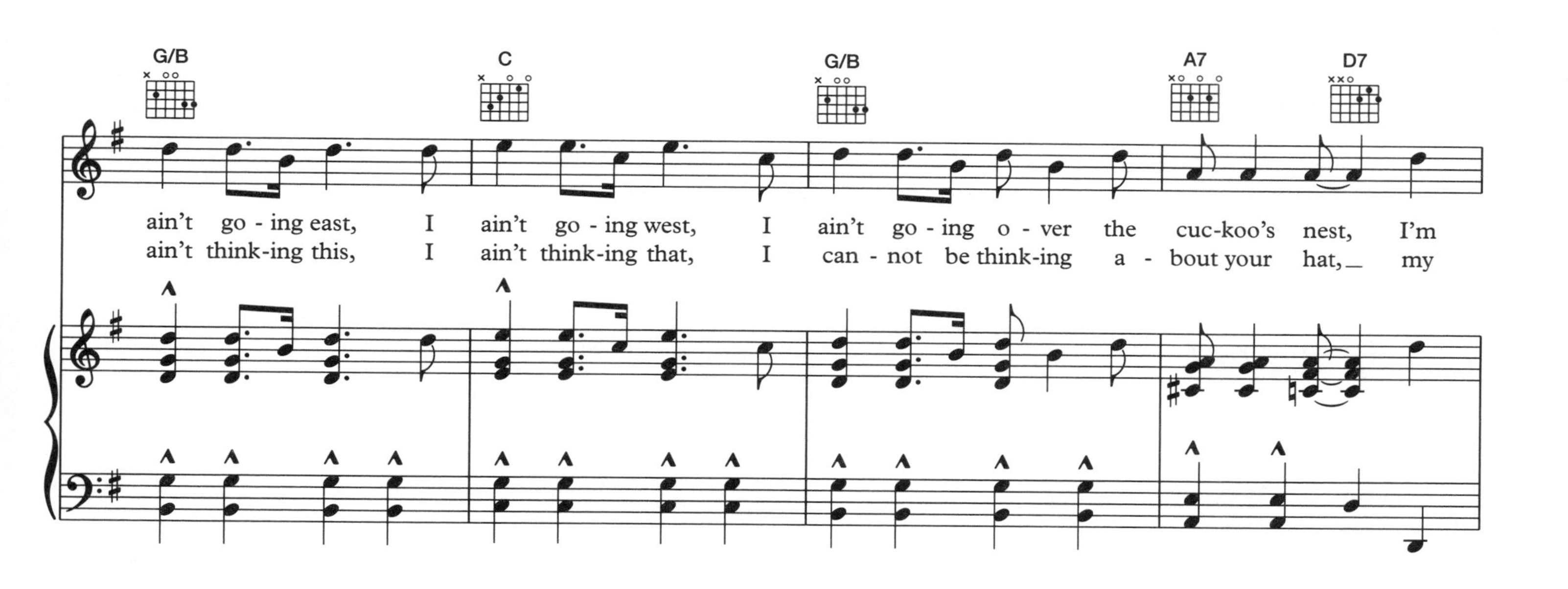
G/B
C
G/B
A7
D7
ain't go - ing east, I ain't go - ing west, I ain't go - ing o - ver the cuc-koo's nest, I'm
ain't think-ing this, I ain't think-ing that, I can - not be think-ing a - bout your hat, my

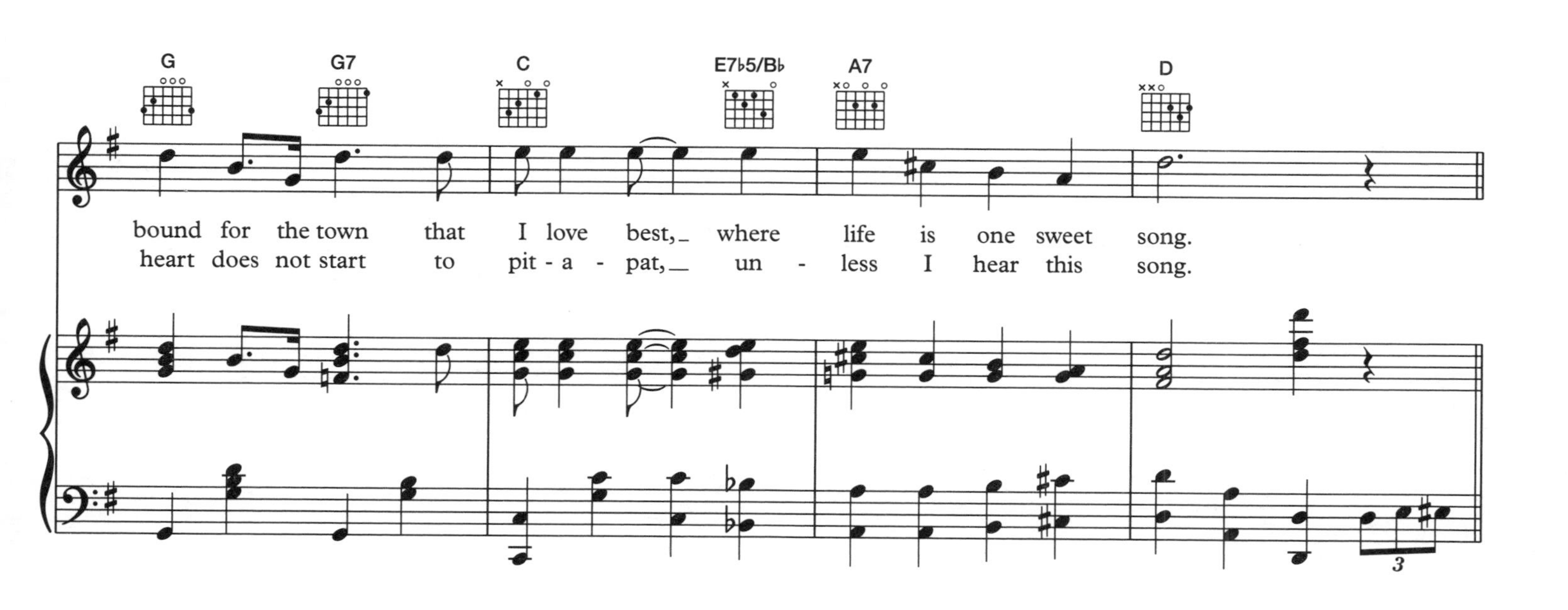
G
G7
C
E7♭5/B♭
A7
D
bound for the town that I love best, where life is one sweet song.
heart does not start to pit - a - pat, un - less I hear this song.

D7
Gmaj9
p–f
Way down yon - der in New Or - leans, in the land of drea - my scenes,
D7
G#dim7
D7
D7#5
G
there's a gar - den of E - den, that's what I mean.
D7
Gmaj9
Cre - ole ba - bies with flash - ing eyes, soft - ly whis - per with ten - der sighs.
G7
C6
Gaug
C6
Stop! Oh! won't you give your la - dy fair a lit - tle smile.
fz

A7 D7 Ddim7
Stop! You bet your life you'll lin - ger there, a lit - tle
fz
3
D7 G Em
while. There is hea - ven right here on earth,
G E♭7 G D7
with those beau - ti-ful queens, way down yon - der in New Or -
1. 2. to patter
G F♯/C♯ D7/C G D7 A♯dim G G7
D.𝄋
Fine
- leans. The

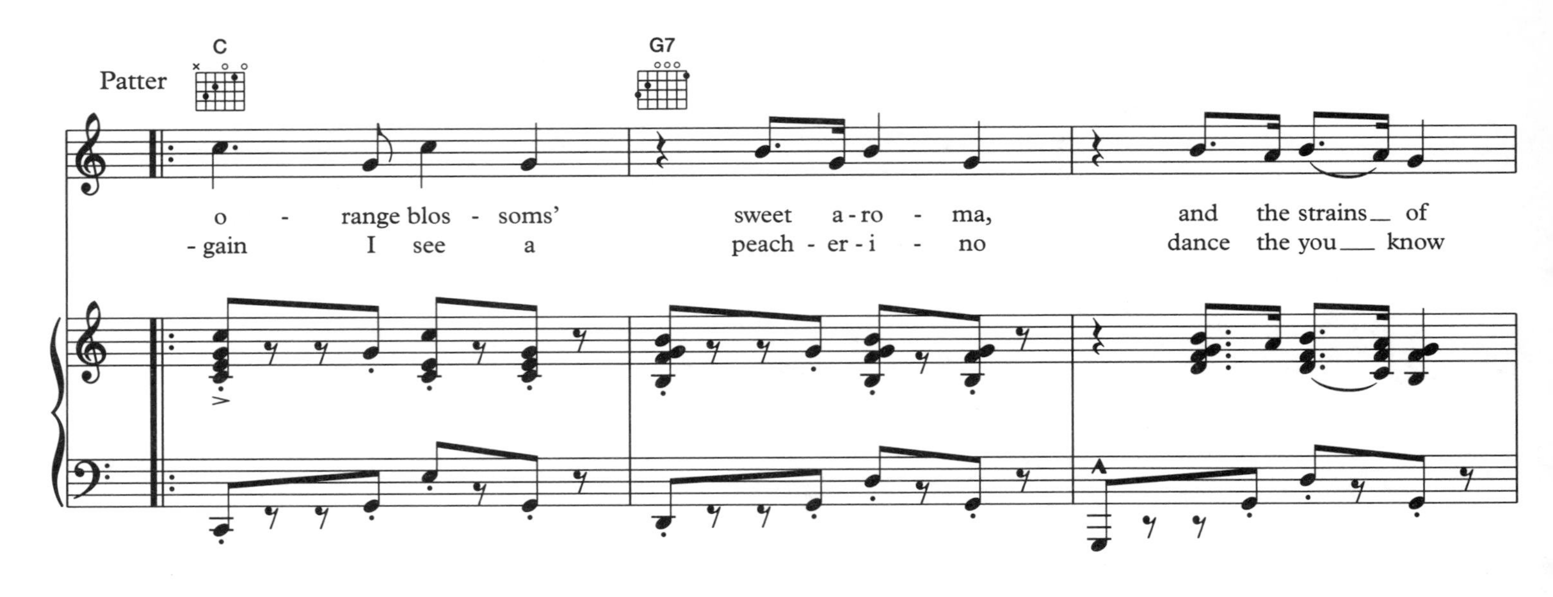
Patter
C
G7
o - range blos - soms' sweet a-ro - ma, and the strains of
-gain I see a peach-er-i - no dance the you know

C
G7
La Pa-lo - ma, seem to throw me in - to a co - ma,
what I mean - o, she could shake a mean tam - bou-ri - no,

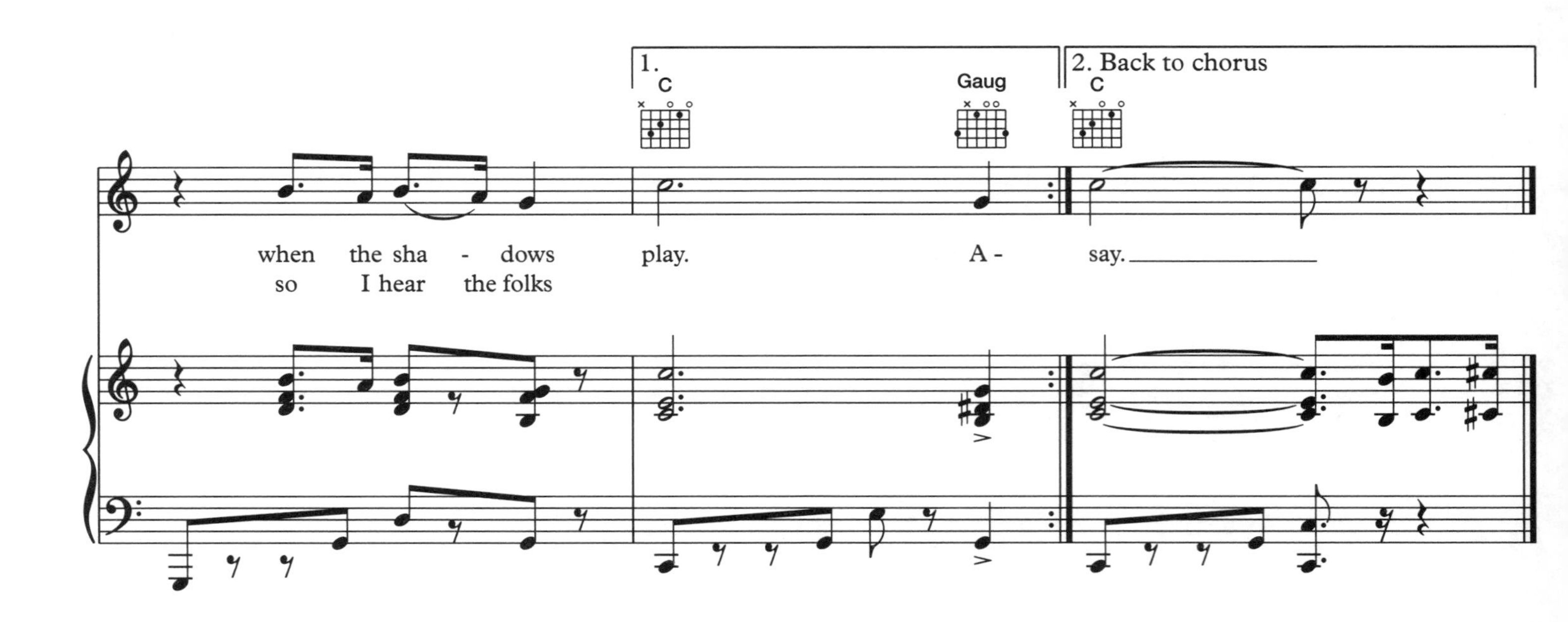
1.
2. Back to chorus
C
Gaug
C
when the sha - dows play. A - say.
so I hear the folks

S'POSIN'

Words by ANDY RAZAF
Music by PAUL DENNIKER

Am
F7
A7
D7
guess it, got to make my feel-ings known some - how.
-bove you to be true to you and you a - lone.
G
D11
D7
S'po-sin' I should fall in love with you,
p-f
G
C#dim7
3fr
D11
D7
G
do you think that you could love me too?
S'po-sin' I should
Bm/F#
Em
A7
hold you and ca - ress you, would it im - press you, or dis -

D13
5fr
D7
3fr
D11
D7
G
D11
-tress you?
S'po-sin' I should say, 'For you I yearn',
D7
G
G7
G13
C6
B7
would you think I'm speak-ing out of turn?
And
Em
G7/F
Edim7
Cm6/E♭
B7
Em
A7
G/D
s'po-sin' I'd de-clare it, would you take my love and share it?
I'm not s'po-sin',
fz
D7
1.
G
Gmaj7
C6/G
D7/G
2.
G
C6/G
D7/G
G
D.𝄋
I'm in love with you.
you.

WHAT IS THIS THING CALLED LOVE?

Words and Music by COLE PORTER

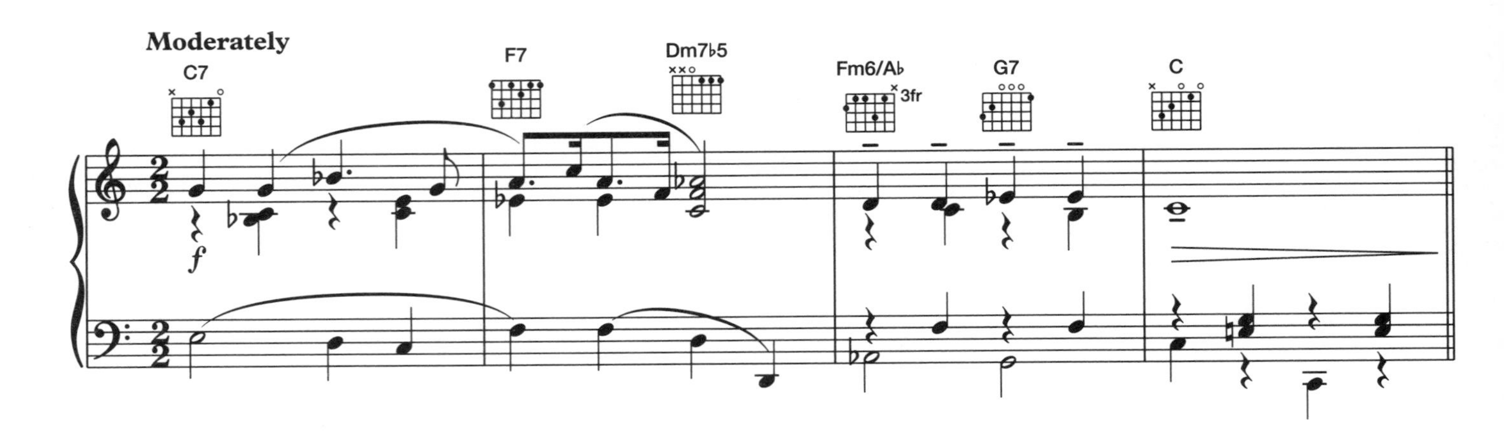

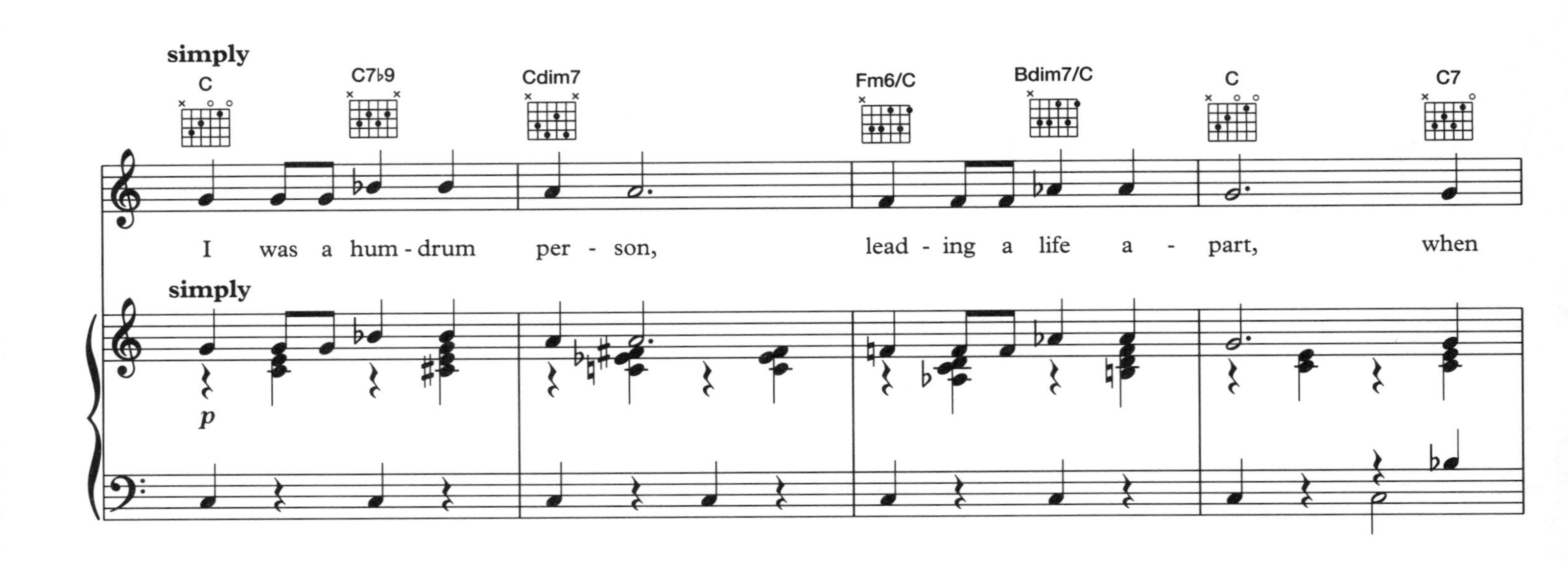

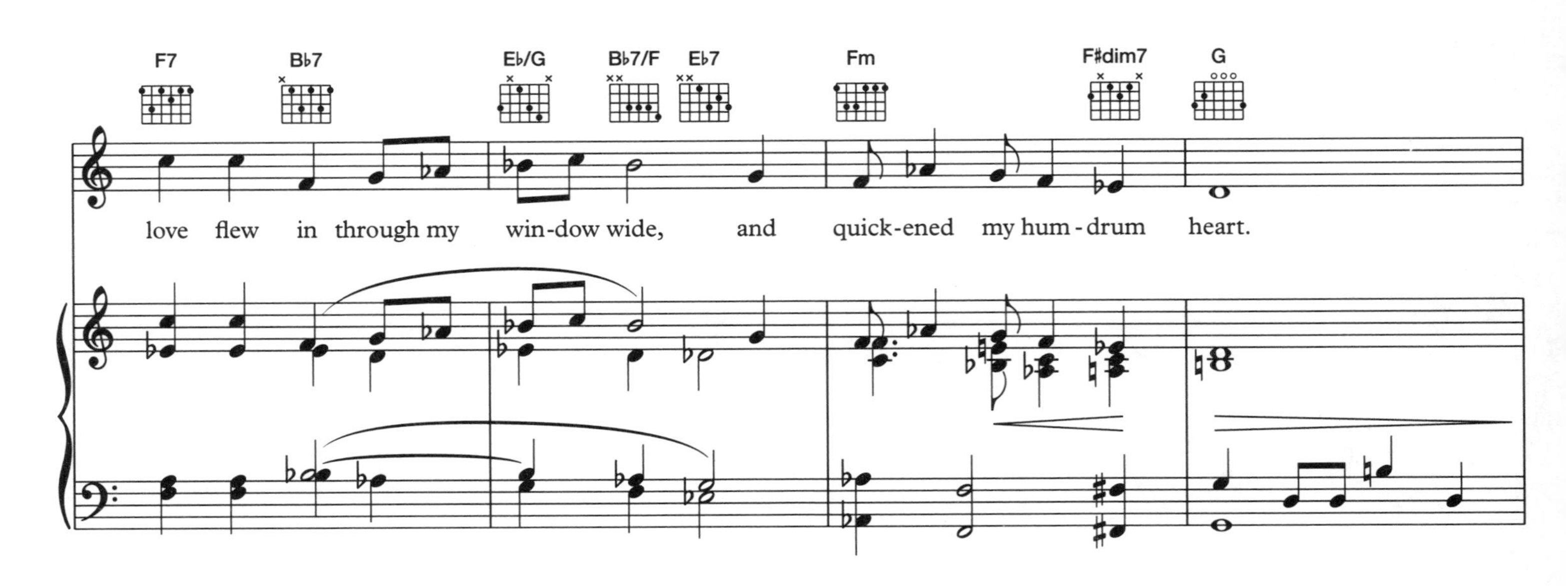

A7/G
Cm6/G
D7/G
G
G7/F
Love flew in through my win - dow, I was so hap - py then, but
C7
F7
Dm7♭5
Fm6/A♭
G7♯5
C
af - ter love had stayed a lit - tle while, love flew out a - gain.
slow blues
Dm7/A
G13
C
C7
What is this thing called
mp – mf
marked
Fm6/C
G7
G7♯5
love? This fun - ny thing called

C
Cmaj7
C6
C
C7
C7♭9
love? Just who can solve its mys - te -
Fm6/C
G7
G7♯5
- ry? Why should it make a fool of
C
C7
Fm
C
Cm
3fr
F7
me? I saw you there one won - der - ful
B♭
A♭
4fr
A♭aug
A♭6
4fr
Fm7
day, you took my heart and threw it a -
3

G
Cm6/G
G7/B
N.C.
C
C7♭9
Cdim7
-way.
That's why I ask the Lord in hea-ven a-

Fm6/C
G7
G7♯5
-bove,
what is this thing called

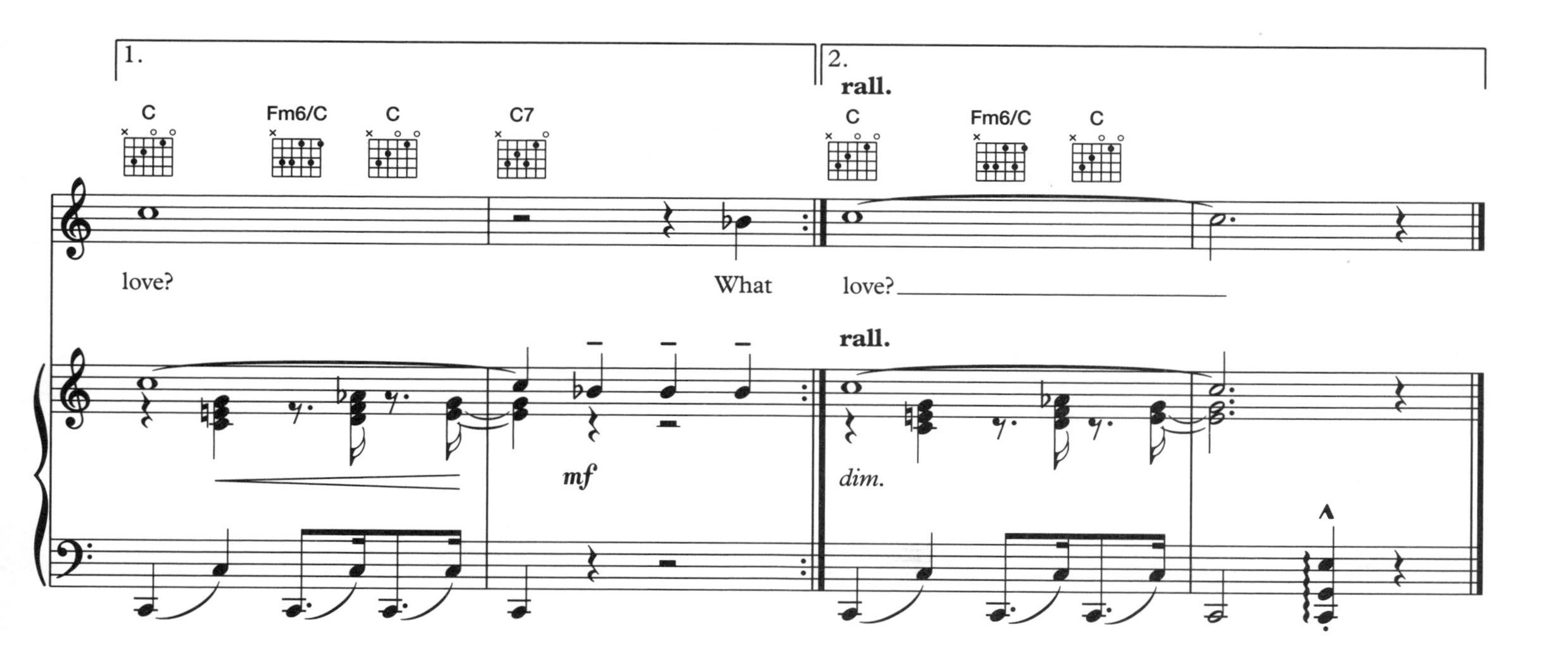
1.
2.
rall.
C
Fm6/C
C
C7
C
Fm6/C
C
love?
What
love?
rall.
mf
dim.

WHEN YOU'RE SMILING

Words and Music by MARK FISHER,
JOE GOODWIN and LARRY SHAY

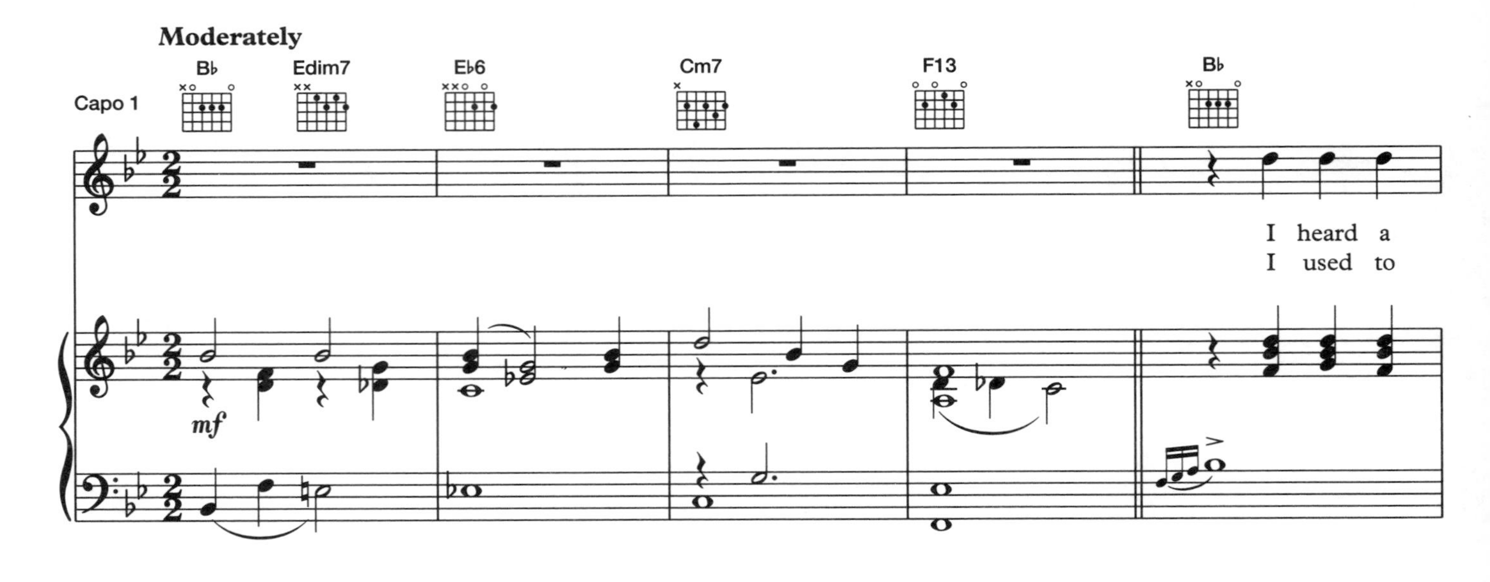

G9/D G7♭5/D♭ F F♯dim7 C7 F7
smile', then he start - ed sing - ing this song.
right, and you'll ne - ver hear me com - plain. When you're
B♭ B♭maj7 B♭ G7
smil - ing, when you're smil - ing, the whole world
Cm
smiles with you, when you're laugh - ing, when you're
Cm7 F7 F7♯5 B♭
laugh - ing, the sun comes shin - ing through,

B♭dim7
B♭
B♭7
B♭7♯5/F♯
E♭/G
F♯dim7
E♭/G
F♯dim
E♭/B♭
but when you're cry - ing,
you bring on the rain,
so stop your
C7
C9
F7
G♯dim7
F7
B♭
sigh - ing,
be hap - py a - gain.
Keep on smil - ing
B♭7/A♭
G7
INTRO:
Cm/G
E♭m/G♭
F7
F13
'cause when you're smil - ing,
the whole world smiles with
1.
2.
B♭
D♭dim7
Cm7
F7
B♭
Cm7
F13♭9
B♭6/9
D.C.
you.
When you're
you.

WHO'S SORRY NOW?

Words by BERT KALMAR and HARRY RUBY
Music by TED SNYDER

B♭m F/C C7 F7 F11/G F7 F11 F7
now, while I am just learn - ing to smile.
- gret, and now you know just how it feels.
B♭ D7 Gaug G7
Who's sor - ry now? Who's sor - ry now? Whose heart is
p - mf
D7/A G7/B C7 F7
ach - ing for break - ing each vow? Who's sad and blue?
B♭ Bdim7 F/C C7 F7 F11/G
Who's cry - ing too, just like I cried o - ver you?

F7 F11 F7 B♭ D7
— Right to the end, just like a friend,
Gaug G7 G7 Gaug G7 Cm G7 Cm
I tried to warn you some - how.
You had your
Cm7♭5 B♭/F G7 C7 E♭m/G♭ F7
way, now you must pay, I'm glad that you're sor - ry
1. B♭ Bdim7 F7/C F11 F7
now.
2. B♭ F13sus4 B♭
now.
D.C.
3
f

YOU DO SOMETHING TO ME

Words and Music by COLE PORTER

E♭m/G E♭7/G A♭m 3fr E♭m/G♭ F7 Gm Gm7/F
dear, why, when you ap - pear, some-thing hap - pens
now, and I'm sure some - how, of this trans - for -
mf
p
C9/E E♭dim7 Dm7♭5 C7 Fm poco rit. B7 B♭7
to me, and the stran - gest feel - ing goes through me?
-ma - tion there can be but one ex - pla - na - tion.
poco rit.
a tempo
E♭ D/E♭ E♭6 E♭maj9 D/B♭ E♭6
You do some - thing to me,
a tempo
p-mf
Edim7 B♭7
some - thing that sim - ply mys - ti - fies me.

Fm
B♭dim7
Fm
Fm7♭5
C7
Tell me, why should it be,
F9
B♭7
F♯dim7
you have the power to hyp - no - tize me?
E♭/G
F♯dim7
B♭7
C7
Let me live 'neath your spell,
B/D♯
B♭/D
D♭dim7
A♭/C
A♭m/C♭
do do that voo - doo that you do so
mf

Bb6
Eb
D/Eb
well, for you do
p

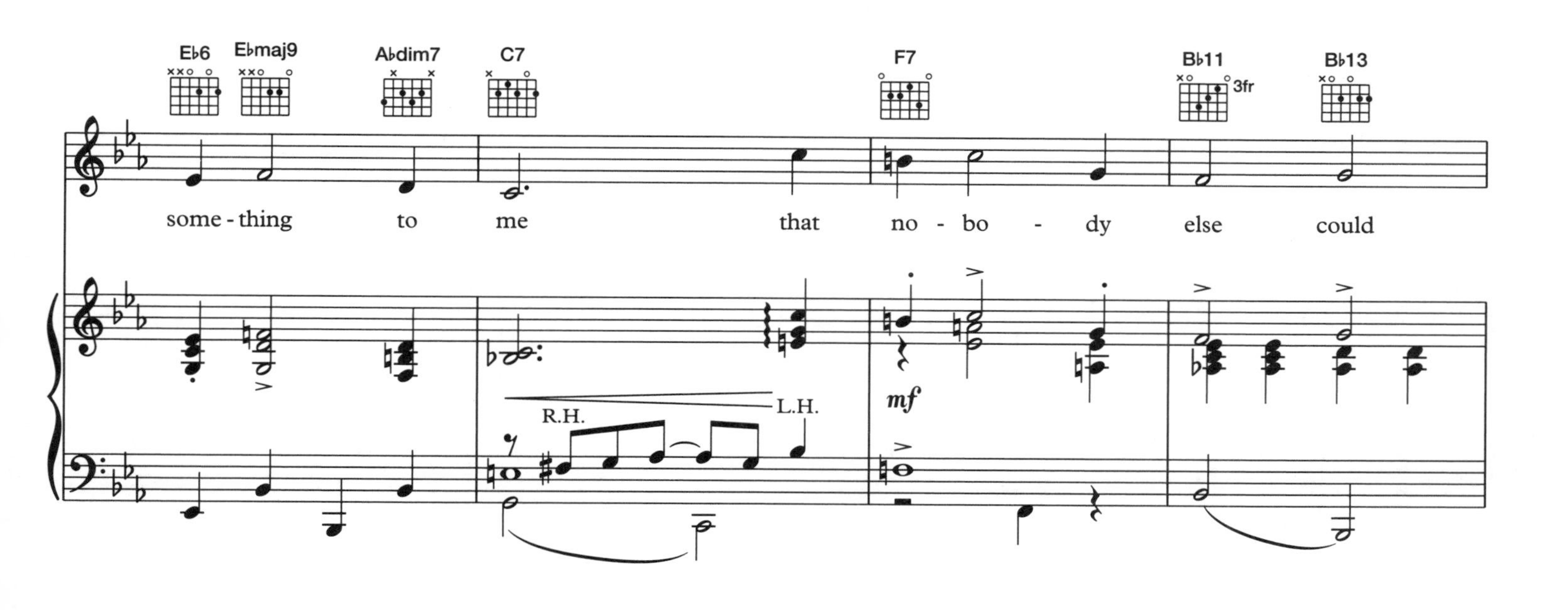

Eb6
Ebmaj9
Abdim7
C7
F7
Bb11
3fr
Bb13
some - thing to me that no - bo - dy else could
R.H.
L.H.
mf

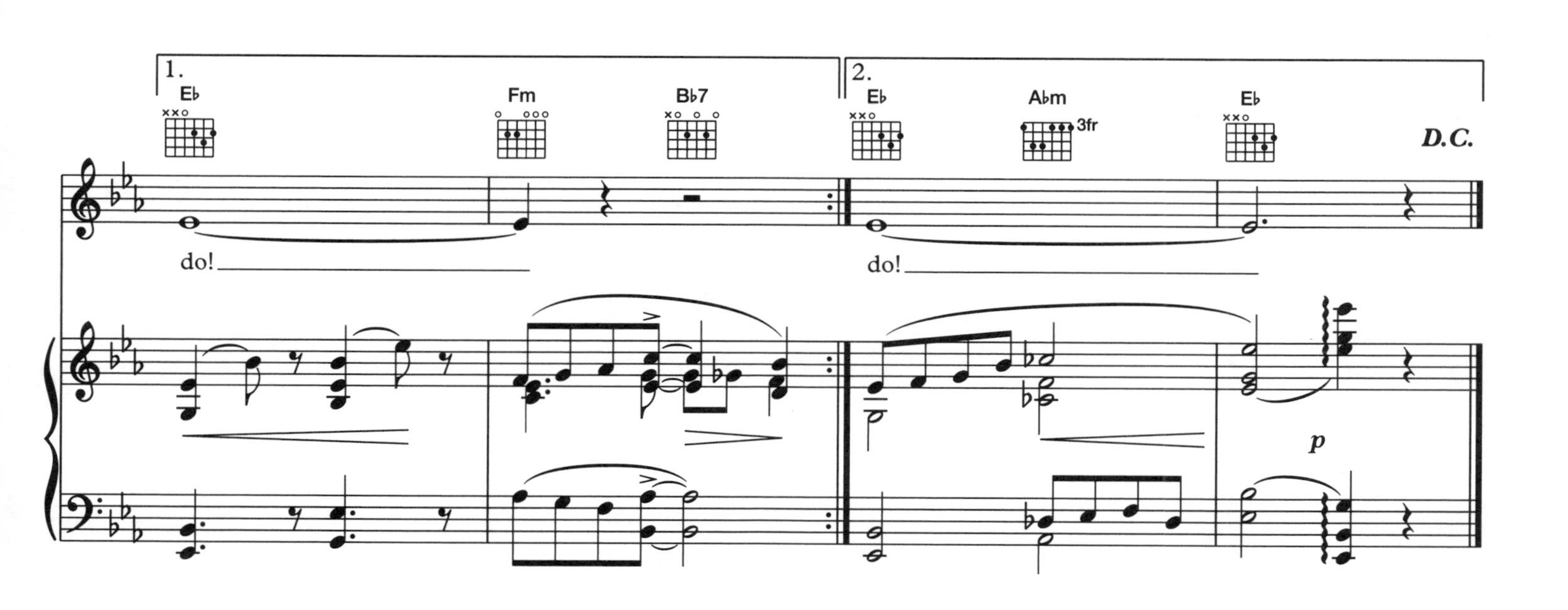

1.
2.
Eb
Fm
Bb7
Eb
Abm
3fr
Eb
D.C.
do!
do!
p

YOU'RE IN KENTUCKY SURE AS YOU'RE BORN

Words and Music by GEORGE A LITTLE,
HAVEN GILLESPIE and LARRY SHAY

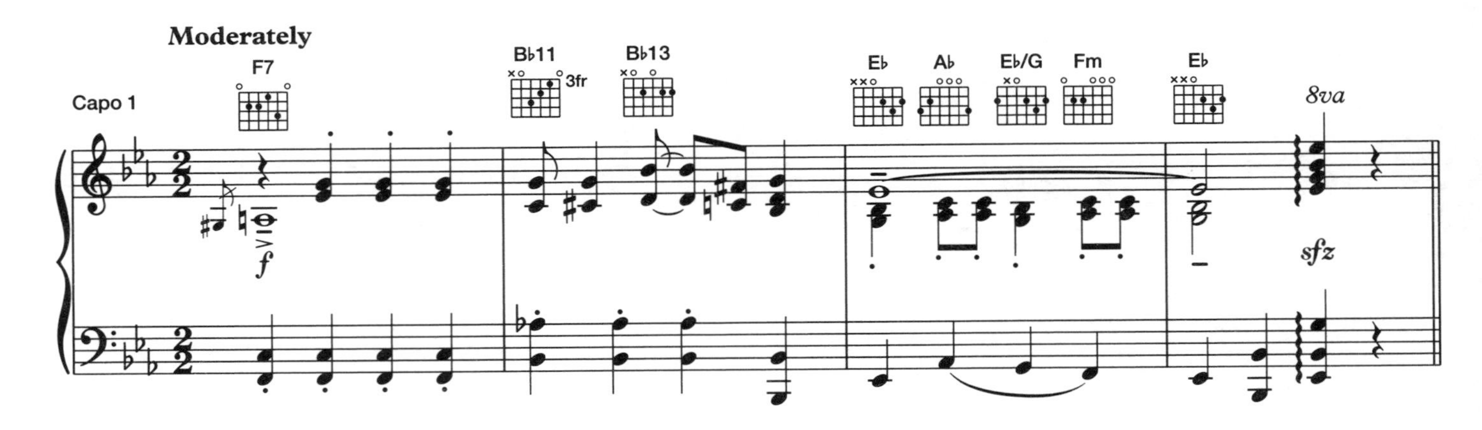

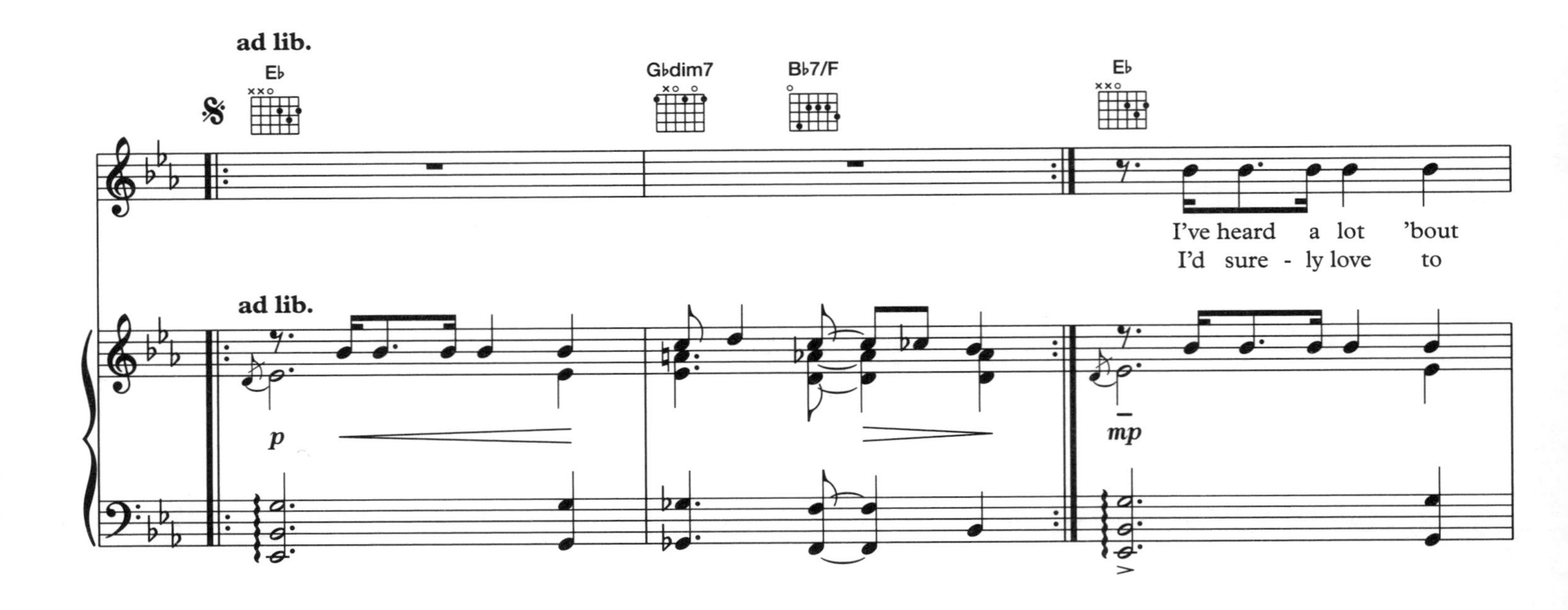

F9
B♭11
3fr
B♭13
E♭
B♭7♯5
as my Ken - tuc - ky home sweet home.
of my Ken - tuc - ky home sweet home.
E♭
G♭dim7
B♭7/F
You'll sure be-lieve just what I say, if you should ev - er
Just put me on a rail-road track, won't need no train to
C7
F9
B♭11
3fr
B♭13
stray some day down to my old Ken - tuc - ky
take me back to my Ken - tuc - ky home sweet
E♭
D♭dim7
F7
F7♯5
home. It won't be hard to
home. If you go down there some

158
B♭ F7/C B♭/D C♯dim7 B♭/D G♭7/D♭ C7 F7 B♭dim B♭7
find, if you'll keep this on your mind. When you
day, please re - mem - ber what I say.
E♭maj7 D7 Fm
see a field where grass is blue, and ev - ery - thing looks
mf
C7 F9 B♭11 3fr B♭13
good to you, you're in Ken - tuc - ky, sure as you're
3
E♭ E♭maj7
born. When a mil - lion sun - beams

D7
Fm
C7
light your way, says, 'Come on stran - ger, won't you stay?',
F9
B♭11
3fr
B♭13
E♭
you're in Ken - tuc - ky, sure as you're born.
E♭7
When the sha - dows creep, you can go to sleep
A♭
C7
on a car - pet of moon - beams, you can dream your dreams,

Printed in Great Britain by Hobbs the Printers Ltd, Totton, Hampshire 9/97